CONTENTS

Indica

1 - Along Came Mary   1

2 - Panama Red   7

3 - Papa's Got A Brand New Bag   13

4 - Leaving On A Jet Plane   26

5 - In-A-Gadda-Da-Vida   30

6 - Georgia On My Mind   34

7 - White Wedding   52

8 - For The Love Of Money   57

9 - Cocaine   61

10 - Witchy Woman   66

11 - Take It To The Limit   82

12 - Summertime   84

13 - Mercedes-Benz   89

14 - People Get Ready   95

15 - White Lines   100

16 - Homegrown   102

17 - Ride Like the Wind   108

18 - Jamaica Jerk Off   111

19 - Johnny Too Bad   117

20 - Roll With It   125

21 - White Cliffs Of Dover   130

22 - Patience   133

23 - What'd I Say   139

24 - I Don't Want To Miss A Thing   142

25 - I'm Your Captain   148

26 - I Did It My Way   158

INDICA

Indie in
Jamaica

The story of Steven James, the first person
ever to grow Indica Marijuana in Jamaica

by

Steve Daniel &
Alex Edwards

1st Edition December 2015

ISBN: 978-0-578-30088-7

Thanks to Helen Jane Oliver for your
editorial contributions.

*People's lives are made up of the times they live
in, the people they meet, the opportunities they take
advantage of, and the risks they are willing to take.*

*The events written about in this book actually
happened, if I didn't make them all up...*

1 - ALONG CAME MARY

The first joint I ever saw in my whole life, I rolled. It was the summer of 1964. In a month and a half, I would be thirteen years old and starting the eighth grade. The country was in the grip of the British Invasion, but in the Valley, the small community in rural north Georgia where I grew up, you were more likely to hear Buck Owens on the radio than The Rolling Stones.

I lived on a long, two-lane rural route that ran through humid farmland twenty miles south of the industrial smog of Chattanooga, Tennessee. The houses on the road were old, scattered, and few. I lived in a farmhouse that sat on a couple of acres of land that had a creek running through it. We had two horses and a jon boat.

Effie was our housekeeper. She was a stout, forceful woman and, as much as anyone else, she raised me. I was a hyperactive kid and never had more fun than when I was causing alarm and demanding attention through some orchestrated troublemaking. I felt compelled to push boundaries, and knew that I found them when I got whipped. My parents, grandparents, aunts, uncles, and cousins were always whipping me for something. Effie also had license to whip me. When I was three or four years old, she was the one who most effectively scared me into behaving, but usually only in the short run.

"Steven James! *Steven James!* When I catch you, I'm going to whip the white off your butt 'til you're black as me!" she would yell and swing at me with whatever happened to be handy. Once she raised a knot on my forehead with a frozen steak. By the time I was twelve, her threats and warnings had lost a lot of their charge. In the summertime, it was easier to stay out of the house and out of the way.

The businesses along my road catered mainly to the meager needs of farmers and foundry workers. Across the street from my house was a small grocery store run by an old woman named Gladys Helton. Her two grandsons, Johnny and Bobby, visited her for two weeks, twice a year. Johnny was two years older than me, and Bobby was two years younger. Their father was a Lieutenant Commander in the Navy and stationed in the Panama Canal Zone.

During their summer visits, Johnny and Bobby and I would get up early and get together at their grandmother's house or my house. We would ride the horses across the field and down to the creek. Bobby was small enough that he and I fit on one horse. All three of us fit in the jon boat, and we went fishing a lot.

We had the deep, dirty tans of boys who stay outside shirtless in the sun. For two weeks, we seldom had to explain ourselves to anyone. We didn't have curfews. After we left the house in the morning, we sometimes didn't come in until after midnight. Our families were just as happy to have us out of the house and making noise elsewhere. We let each other be.

If we wanted to campout, we did. We pitched a tent out in the field, and by flashlight we looked at Playboys that we had managed to steal and the occasional lesbian bondage novel, which Johnny and Bobby had access to because they lived on a Naval base.

Johnny, by default of being the oldest, seemed hip and worldly. He was ahead of Bobby and me on every important subject: girls, music, how to dress, what to say. He was really into the British bands and did his best with what he had to signify that. He had sandy colored bangs that hung in a sharp diagonal across his forehead, but the sides and the back were too short to look authentically mod. Even so, he was the coolest kid I knew.

"You know how to roll a cigarette?" he said on the third morning of their visit. We were sitting on the bank at a bend in the creek that was covered on both sides by deep woods.

"Yeah," I said, "My daddy rolls his own."

"Go and get one of his cigarette papers and bring it back here," said Johnny, "Get a few."

I went off and got them, happy to be on a mission. When I got back, Johnny handed me a bag of marijuana that he brought with him from the Panama Canal Zone, and I rolled a joint. It was the first I had ever seen.

Every day after that, for the rest of their visit, we did the same thing: rode the horses out to the creek and smoked pot. The first two times I didn't get high, but it was fun just the same because it was exotic and illegal. However, I knew I was missing something that Johnny and Bobby were getting. The third time, I was sitting on my horse smoking a joint at the bend in the creek, and all at once I knew what getting high was all about.

I stood up, balanced on the horse's back, and jumped off into the cold clear water. I came up laughing. I didn't know it was possible for a person to feel the way I felt. I also didn't know what I was laughing at, but I couldn't stop.

Johnny started singing "Walk Right In," which had been a hit for the Rooftop Singers a year before. I had never heard anything so beautiful and true in my life as his voice carrying across the creek and past the leaves and into the crystalline day. Bobby and I laughed and sang too.

"We're like bandits," he said.

"Yeah, we're like pirates," I said and dove under the surface of the water.

A couple days later, we were sitting on some warm rocks, slowly drying out in a sunny spot on the bank. We were getting stoned, and when I passed the joint to Johnny, he said, "Do you know anybody who would want to buy some?"

"Some what?" I said. "Pot?"

"Yeah," he said.

I said, "Sure. I know some guys who play in a rock n' roll band.

They probably want some."

He said, "okay," and inhaled, squinting his eyes like he was in deep thought.

A couple of miles down the two-lane highway from where I lived were two brand new subdivisions, one on either side of the road. Each subdivision had a rock n' roll band comprised of teenage boys who lived there. In both subdivisions, the streets, the split-level ranch houses, and the rock bands who practiced in their garages were practically identical. Kids rode bikes and shot baskets in the driveways of the mortgaged palaces of the young professional class. The neat, green lawns came right to the streets.

The guys in the garage bands were older than me, and some of them were even older than Johnny. I didn't know any of them personally, but I knew some of the younger kids in the subdivisions who went to my junior high school. They all had bikes. Sometimes, a group of guys would ride down to my house to swim in the creek. They always had to be back home by dark, and, if they ever camped out it was only after a complicated phone relay with promises and pleading.

From this group, the least encumbered by such authoritative entanglements were the three Profit brothers. They lived with their dad and step-mom and were the first children of divorce that I ever knew.

They rode their bikes around all over the place, miles from the subdivisions. I told them that I had a proposition for them.

The oldest, Kevin, was thirteen, Andrew was ten or eleven, and Ronnie was eight. Ronnie stood out from his brothers, not just because he was the youngest and smallest and almost never said anything, but also because his hair was a thick pile of tangled curls. Their father insisted he keep it cut short, but even so, it was bushy and weird.

Johnny, Bobby, and I broke up into smaller bags the few ounces of pot they had brought with them from Panama. We gave a handful of the bags to the Profit brothers to sell to the guys in their neighborhood rock bands. The market was ripe, and the Profit brothers sold the bags easily. The teens who would gather in the garages to watch the rock bands bash away at songs by The Searchers and The Zombies also bought bags.

By the end of Johnny and Bobby's visit, we had sold almost all the pot. They went back to the Panama Canal Zone, and I hung onto what was left. Standing in their grandmother's, humid driveway, I said goodbye while Lieutenant Commander Helton loaded suitcases into the back of the car.

"We'll bring more when we come back at Christmastime," said Johnny with a cool flip of his bangs. We shook on it.

"Tell Effie I'm sorry about spilling the iced tea," said Bobby.

"It's okay," I said. "She just hollers like that."

"Let's go, boys!" called their father, "We're gonna be late."

I walked back across the highway by myself. That afternoon, I went to the creek, but I didn't feel like swimming. I rolled a joint and smoked it while I looked at the clear water. I laid back and looked up through the leaves at the late summer sky. I wondered how high up Johnny and Bobby were. Then, I wondered what eighth grade would be like and dozed off listening to the robins sing.

A week before Christmas, Johnny and Bobby returned, and, as Johnny promised, they brought back more marijuana. The three of us were upstairs in the drafty bedroom that he and his brother used in his grandmother's house. Johnny opened his heavy, canvas, Government Issue duffle bag.

"Ho, ho, ho!" he said as he pulled out sweaters and shirts and socks. Underneath was a large rectangular package.

"It's a whole kilo," he said.

"How much is that?" I asked.

"More than two pounds," Johnny said. "Thirty five ounces."

"Let's get it down to the barn," I said.

"In the morning," said Johnny. His hair had grown out some since the summer, and he gave it a confident shake.

The next day, we settled on a simple measure for breaking up the kilo. We didn't have scales, so we used our fingers. One finger was a nickel bag, two was a dime, three fingers we called a lid, and four fingers was an ounce. The price structure was five dollars a finger, with nickels at five bucks, dimes at ten, lids at fifteen, and ounces at twenty. The beauty of the deal was that the kilo only cost nine dollars. The first dimebag we sold paid for the whole load.

2 - PANAMA RED

"It's Panama Red. Ten bucks," said Kevin to group of high school kids gathered in the game room of one of the houses in one of the subdivisions. He was showing them a handful of dime bags.

"How old is he?" asked a bored looking girl sitting on the floor with a pile of records. She meant Ronnie.

"Eight," he answered for himself.

The guys in the game room pooled their money and bargained with each other and bought the bags.

"Do you have anymore?" said a boy with acne and turtleneck

sweater.

"Yeah," I said before Kevin could answer.

"The Mixed Emotions are playing tonight at April Smith's Christmas party. Come over and bring some more."

The Mixed Emotions were a newly formed garageband in the neighborhood. They specialized in surf instrumentals because they didn't have a microphone. Society Inc. didn't have one either. They were influenced by the English groups and did a good rendition of "Glad All Over" by The Dave Clark Five, instrumental though it was.

I had never been to a party that wasn't an adult-sanctioned, Sunday evening affair. Johnny and I hitched a ride on the back of an old man's truck and hopped off at the subdivisions. It wasn't that far to walk, but it was cold out. The pockets of our coats were stuffed with nickel and dime bags. We could see our breath in the moonlight.

Every house on every block had blinking lights across the front or multi-colored ones around the windows. Wreaths hung from front doors and mailboxes. It was absolutely silent except for the sound of our breathing. April's house was four blocks up a long, slow hill. There was a four-foot high fiberglass Santa Claus in her front yard that was lit from inside. From the driveway, we could hear the muffled treble of the band in the basement, and we went to the side door.

Only a Christmas tree and strands of blinking lights lighted the finished basement. The teenagers, about twenty in all, aped the dances they saw on American Bandstand. The Mixed Emotions were playing a rendition of The Ventures' "Walk, Don't Run" that went on for another five minutes after we arrived.

A card table was set up in the corner. The large bowls of chips and pretzels on it had already been decimated. Red and green striped paper cups, bottles of Coke, 7-Up and ginger ale, and an ice bucket full of water were lined up on the bar.

By the time the Mixed Emotions had exhausted their repertoire and were beginning to repeat numbers for a second or third time, Johnny and I had sold all the weed that we were going to sell.
Apparently, the kid with acne and a turtleneck who invited us to the party hadn't put the word out that we would be there, and hardly anybody had any money.

What we lost in sales, we made up for in promotion. We were invited to two more Christmas parties and a New Year's Eve party that was happening if Larry Estes' parents went out of town. Every boy at the party wanted at least a nickel bag as soon as they collected their allowances from their parents.

Before tonight, none of the fifteen and sixteen year olds in the basement would have given me, at thirteen, the time of day. But suddenly, they were deferential and eager to know me. A pudgy kid in a letter jacket with a flushed red face bought a dime bag. Later, he gathered Kevin, Johnny, and me into a corner and poured bourbon into our sodas from the pint bottle that he had hidden in his jacket. He took a long drink from the bottle while simultaneously keeping his head down.

"Don't tell anybody," he said. He was drunk. "Only me and Doug are supposed to know about it."

"Who's Doug?" I said.

"He's on the football team," said Kevin, who was among peers.

"Second team," clarified the drunk kid.

The party broke up around ten o'clock. Most of the girls were picked up by their fathers to keep them from having to walk home in the cold.

Johnny and I thanked April, who didn't seem won over by us, and said goodbye to Kevin. When we got to the bottom of the long hill, we were disoriented and couldn't tell which way we had come. Block after freezing block, we wandered until we finally found our way back to the highway. In spite of the cold, I liked the walk. I liked knowing that I was seeing the houses in a way that people rarely saw them, least of all the ones lucky enough to live in them. The peaceful, darkened houses had the coiled, potential energy of predatory cats sleeping in cages at the zoo.

We walked all the way back to my house. No cars ever passed for us to catch a ride, but we had been out there so long, forty-five more minutes hardly mattered. It was almost midnight when I got home, and it took me a long time to get to sleep.

1965 was just a week old when Johnny and Bobby flew back to the Panama Canal Zone. We had sold almost the whole kilo.

I stashed the rest, and the Profit brothers and I sold it with no trouble before Johnny and Bobby returned in the summer with twenty kilos.

The day they arrived they brought their duffle bags out to the barn and unloaded the bricks, which smelled faintly of fruit. We broke them down into nickel bags. There were lots of stems that we just pulled out and threw away as we worked in the hot, stagnant, barn air.

We worked until we had made hundreds of nickel bags. Then, we put them all into paper grocery sacks. I put those into an empty, metal, feed drum with a tight fitting lid. I rolled it to the back of the barn and stood it up with the other old barrels and useless, rusted and mud-caked tools hanging up back there. The weed was safely hidden, and the metal barrels kept the rats from eating the weed, which we learned last year that they would do.

The next morning, the three Profit brothers rode their bikes through the thick humidity down to the barn. It was just past eight in the morning, but they were sweating and wiping their faces.

"What's that do?" said Ronnie pointing to an obscure earth-tilling contraption. He was nine then.

"It doesn't do anything. It's rusted," I said.

He went back to stuffing his army surplus backpack with nickel bags. The oppressive humidity made his hair stand out in a crazier way than usual.

"How much is this?" asked Andrew, who just turned twelve, meaning the amount of weed in the barrel.

"That's like 500 nickel bags."

"I'm taking some to baseball practice," he said.

"Not a good idea," said Kevin, the oldest, who was already tying down a full, grocery bag to the back fender of his bike.

"Yeah it is," protested Andrew.

"Hurry up," said Kevin, "It's hot in here."

When all three of them were loaded up, they rode out to the highway and then north to the subdivisions. It felt good to be out of the furnace of the barn. I heard a tractor in the distance, but I didn't see anyone. I went back in the barn, quickly rolled a handful of joints and went to find Johnny and Bobby.

That summer, the number of garage bands in the two subdivisions had grown to five, six if you counted Thom Cain and Doug Roads. They were an acoustic duo who sang Simon & Garfunkle and Everly Brothers songs. The market for nickel bags was booming.

In a matter of a few days, quite a bit of weed was moving around my small community. In small communities, people talk. When Johnny and Bobby flew back to Panama, I still had a lot of pot in the barn and a completely saturated market. Even so, I told them to bring more weed at Christmastime, as much as they could. I didn't know what I was going to do with it, and I immediately started trying to figure that out. It was time to expand, to move beyond the ball fields and the subdivisions into more lucrative, anonymous, and, therefore, safer, territory.

Kevin, Andrew, and Ronnie Profit had all worn out of set a bike tires going from my house to the subdivisions, to the ball fields, to the high school. Replacing the tires was no big deal, since we were all making lots of easy money. Any place that served teenagers and repelled adults, the Profit brothers had visited again and again on their bikes.

They haunted drainage ditches, basements, and dugouts. They had been behind every greasy spoon in the area.

It still wasn't enough. I had to find a place with room to grow.

After the fourth of July 1965, I found it on Big Nine.

3 - PAPA'S GOT A BRAND NEW BAG

Officially, it was Ninth Street in downtown Chattanooga, and, eventually, it was renamed Martin Luther King Boulevard, but growing up I only knew it as Big Nine. There were eighteen nightclubs on Big Nine, arranged symmetrically with nine on either side of the street.

Nicky Shorter was a friend of mine whose father waswell-connected to the local redneck mafia: a twisted vein of dirty blood and dirtier money that connected Jim Crow judges, bootleggers, politicians, attorneys, pimps, and prison snitches. Nicky's dad was a drinking buddy of Sheriff Bookie Turner, who had been re-elected to the position, even as he sat in jail, having been indicted on charges of corruption.

Nicky's dad supplied all the clubs with white alcohol and gambling devices like punch boards and tip boards. He finagled a bogus hardship license for Nicky so that, at fourteen, he could make the deliveries to Big Nine with relative impunity. On Thursdays, he and his father would load their Volkswagen bus with the contraband, and Nicky would deliver it.

One morning, I got a bunch of nickel bags together and put them in a big, paper, grocery sack and walked over to Nicky's house. The steam was rising with the sun.

"Are you going to Big Nine this afternoon?" I asked standing on his squeaky, front porch.

"Yeah, why?" Nicky was about my size, but kind of heavy-set with unfashionably short hair. His eyes were small under a heavy brow, and he had freckles that made it look like his face had been spattered with gutter water. He stood on the other side of the closed screen door.

"I want to go with you."

"What for?"

"I want to help you."

"Doing what?" he said. "I don't need any help."

"I've got all this weed that I want to take over there and sell to the colored folks," I said and held up the paper sack.

Nicky opened the door and came out on the porch. He looked in the bag and said, "What the hell is that?"

"I just told you. It's weed that we can sell on Big Nine."

He laughed. "Hell no," he said. "Where'd you get that?"

"Nevermind that," I said. "Why not?"

"Because if my dad found out he'd about kill me."

"We can be quiet about it," I said keeping my voice low to demonstrate and dramatize the point.

He was still looking in the bag, but now he was frowning thoughtfully.

"Come by and get me before you go," I said and held the bag out for him to take. He didn't move.

"What do I get out of it?" he asked.

I looked into his tiny eyes. "Man, you'll make a dollar a bag," I said.

"What's that gonna come out to?"

"I'm probably gonna sell forty or fifty bags," I said.

"OK," he said and took the bag, "I'll come get you." He went back inside his house, and the screen door clacked shut.

Working men in our area, different than the nearby sub-divisions, our fathers, grandfathers and uncles, were bringing home eighty to one hundred and ten dollars a week from ex-hausting, blue collar labor. So, forty or fifty dollars on a Thurs-day was good money for a fourteen year old. Like his dad, Nicky was tough, kind of dumb, and could be easily bought.

As in casinos and airports, time stopped in the night-clubs on Big Nine. They were perpetually dark inside. Most of the clubs didn't have windows and were dimly illuminated by strands of small, garishly colored light bulbs that turned the mat of cigarette smoke into unearthly colors. The clubs thrived on gambling and tax-free liquor sales and many of them admitted "Members Only." By dint of our illicit and essential business, we were members everywhere.

In the first club, a lanky guy in a t-shirt and apron came from around the bar, and he and Nicky went out to bring in the punch boards and gallons of moonshine.

"What the hell do you want?" said the bartender in a rocky voice, once the door closed. He was a broad man with a big belly.

"I'm with Nicky," I said, "I've got some to weed to sell."

"What are you talking about?"

The bar was nearly empty. One guy sitting alone had been laughing to himself the whole time, and two other guys in sun-glasses were smoking cigarettes and drinking at a table. "Chain

Gang" by Sam Cooke was playing on the jukebox.

"Here." I reached in the sack and handed him a nickel bag. "You can have that one."

He looked down at the bag and then looked at me frowning. Slowly, he put the bag under the bar and just kept staring at me. Nicky and the skinny guy came in carrying boxes, and the bartender nodded them toward the back of the bar where the restrooms, closets, and garbage cans were.

"I'll be back next week," I said, as we left, but the bartender just kept frowning at me.

At our next stop, I was met with the same suspicion and sullen hostility. I never got a harder look than I got from Effie, and as with her, I got used to the attitude. By the time Nicky and I were working our way down the other side of Big Nine, I anticipated the surliness, and I used it the way a tennis player plays against the wall for practice.

I quit taking the whole sack in the and just took a handful of nickels in and approached the manager who was usually also the bartender. I picked up on the fact that they referred to marijuana as "tea." So I started calling it that too.

"You know anybody who wants any tea?"

"What the hell do you know about tea, boy?"

I loved it. I transformed the aggression into something that worked in my favor. The visceral charge that I got from each encounter made me feel wired and totally alive. I would hand them a nickel bag and smile and tell them that that one was on the house.

The clubs were unvarying in their clientele and decor.

At that hour, in the late afternoon, it was mostly men of working age. They wore either work shirts and boots or narrow cut suits with candy-colored shirts. The women that I did see were modest and clearly attached to a man. They sat quietly in smoky concrete boxes drinking and mumbling or not.

Occasionally, before I had a chance to make my introduction, men in the bars would ask what I had in the bag.

"Reefer," I said. I didn't think anything of reaching in the sack and putting the weed on the bar. If the guy didn't have money, I told him he could keep it. "I'll be back next Thursday with some more," I said. "If you've got some money."

We moved the bus from one side of the street to the other and by the last stop, the street was beginning to fill with slowly moving cars. As the sun set, the men and women on the sidewalk were younger, more smartly dressed. They laughed and shouted at one another.

I was getting more comfortable approaching a group of guys on the sidewalk. I liked the looks on their faces when they were confronted with the bizarre and rare proposition of buying tea from a cracker boy on the street. My approach was inelegant, but it was also uncomplicated and fast. I just reached in my pocket and handed them the bags. I enjoyed the rush of power and respect that came with each handoff.

The shadows were an hour longer than when we had started. Everyone from the swampy Southeast is sensitive to the subtleties of atmosphere that accompany even the smallest drop in the temperature and relative humidity. It felt like relief.

We rode back to the Valley, feeling proud of ourselves. At least, that's how I felt. I sold thirty-five nickel bags and gave eighteen away.
Nicky was happy to get his cut, which he insisted on having

that night. I counted out his thirty-five dollars and jumped out of the bus at the end of my driveway.

"Next week," I said.

He nodded and sputtered away.

I went in the house to see if there was anything for dinner.

The following Thursday, late in the afternoon, Nicky picked me up and we went back to Big Nine. This time, everybody had his money ready. At each establishment, we would drop off a gallon or two of whisky and a dozen punch boards. Then, I would go get my grocery sack. It became my calling card.

"Hey Nicky," said a man with grey hair who was sitting in the same place that he had been last week, "Who's that you got with you?"

On the way over we had heard the new James Brown song on the radio, and Nicky said, "That's Papa."

To make sure everybody got it, I said, "Yeah, Papa's got a brand new bag."

That served as enough of an answer and the nickname stuck.

Within a few weeks, I was well known enough that I didn't have to give any more bags away. On Big Nine, I was known by my white skin and my brand new bag of red weed.

"Here comes Papa," guys would yell, when they saw me riding shotgun in Nicky's bus.

"You got me some Lucky Thirteen?" they called out. "Lucky Thirteen" was slang for marijuana that was particular to Big Nine, "M" being the thirteenth letter of the alphabet.

Between the high fives and the handoffs was the unspoken, but no less understood, contract that should we come to any harm, Nicky's dad would come to Big Nine and settle things. Messing with us or ripping us off wouldn't be worth the inevitable and deadly reprisal. Nor would an unlicensed nightclub full of shotgunned blacks stir the judges very much. Everybody understood the structure; it was ingrained in all of us. Nicky and I were on top. We walked on Big Nine with a lot of swagger.

When Johnny and Bobby came back that year for Christmas, they brought fifty kilos of weed. I bought the whole load for 2,000 dollars. They were still paying nine dollars a kilo and I paid them forty bucks a kilo and they were out of the loop after that. I told them that all they had to do was get the weed to me, and I would buy whatever they had. That arrangement was easiest, and made everybody happy.

Between them, the three Profit brothers, and Nicky, it was beginning to get complicated remembering who was in for how much money. Cash up front streamlined everything and suited everybody. When Johnny and Bobby went back to Panama after the New Year, I gave them money to buy the next load.

Buying and selling were as thick in my blood as the red clay in the Georgia earth. I was the last in a line of men inclined toward intoxication, competition, and risk. So far, none of them had been able to turn that combination into money.

Keeping money, once it was made, seemed to require an elusive matrix of psychology and heredity that missed us. My family in the Valley and the fathers of friends in the subdivisions, the drivers of tractors and Cadillacs alike, worked for heavily taxed wages making other men rich. Their time was not their own, and they couldn't easily relate to a man whose time and motivation were his own, or a boy who asked for a fire-proof safe for his fourteenth birthday, like me.

It weighed one hundred pounds empty and was the top of the line in fireproof home safes. My parents, grandparents, aunts and uncles all chipped in on it. And while they did regard the request as peculiar, nobody but Effie asked any questions.

"What are you gonna do with that safe?" she said with a thick hand on her hip.

I laughed. "What does anybody do with a safe?"

"You don't have nothing to put in it," she said.

"Yeah, I do."

"Like what?"

"You'll never know," I said and gave her a shit-eating grin.

"Boy, just because you're fourteen you ain't too old for me to whip," she said as I wrestled the safe up the stairs.

That night, across the creek, I dug up the jar full of money that I had hidden under the root ball of a fallen, rotting Oak tree. Back in my bedroom, I wiped my hands off on my jeans and locked the jar in the safe feeling like a real businessman.

After six months of going to Big Nine on Thursday afternoons with Nicky, I got to be well-known and well-liked there. The guys on the street would greet me, whether they were buying anything or not. Usually they were. There was never a question that the club owners were buying.

One dim, January afternoon, I was in the office of the High

Note Lounge, one of the more well-appointed clubs on Big Nine. A stocky man with even brown skin and white hair that circled a bald head faced me across his desk. On top of the desk were hundreds of small Diamond matchboxes.

He explained how he had his nephew break down each nickel bag into five matchboxes, which he sold for two dollars a piece, doubling his investment. Other clubs also had redistribution methods with huge markups.

"Y'all coming to the James Brown concert?" said a thin drunk named Charles who was always sitting alone on the same stool at the Blue Note, a club known for Bessie Smith style blues.

"Hell no," I said.

"Why not?"

"What business do we have at a James Brown concert?" said Nicky.

"Man, they don't even have white cops up there," I said and it was true. White policemen were refusing to work the show.

"Oh, I thought you was Papa," said Charles laughing drunkenly. "I thought you was a big man."

"You don't need no police," said Bert, the owner of B's. "I'm going. Y'all come with me. You'll be alright."

Nicky and I looked at each other. The idea was tempting.

Surely, there were good times to be had and money to be made at such an event, but I wasn't sure the immunity to personal harm that we enjoyed on Big Nine extended all the way to downtown Chattanooga and the Memorial Auditorium.

"We'll put you boys between some big sisters," he said.

Charles laughed some more.

"Some really big sisters," Bert added.

Nicky and I laughed to cover our apprehension.

The night of the concert, I rolled a bunch of joints to take with me. Nicky and I met Bert and his date and the two big sisters. They might have been sisters to one another, but they definitely weren't Bert's sisters. In their heels, they were taller than him by six inches and taller than Nicky and me by at least eight. The women were also twice our ages and their dresses barely contained their massive breasts and wide hips. Just as Bert said, Nicky and I walked between them. Bert was getting a kick out of it, and the women acted like it was perfectly normal, and they were enjoying it.

"What you doin' with them little white boys?" men called out as we slowly made our way up the crowded sidewalks to the auditorium. I handed them joints, which served as a sufficient explanation.

The men in the crowd wore florid suits with skinny, black neckties. Their lizard leather shoes showed immaculate polish. The women were dressed much like our companions, though few were as exposed. Some wore rabbit fur coats with the collars turned up against the cold night air. I hadn't seen people dressed as nicely in church.

By the time we reached the entrance of the auditorium, I had given away half of the joints that I brought with me, leaving me with about twenty. A dark-skinned, uniformed policeman put out his arm and stopped us as we approached.

"What the hell is this?" he said looking above my head.

"What is what?" said Nicky's big sister even though it was obvious. Her attitude was playful enough, but I didn't want to stand there rapping with cops anymore than necessary. My nervousness was palpable.

The policeman scoffed, shook his head and said, "Y'all are the damndest looking group I ever seen." Then, he smiled at Nicky and me and said, "Don't looked so worried. You'll be fine in there. Go on in and have fun."

I tried not to look like I had a jacket full of joints and forced my face into what I hoped was a normal-looking smile, not guilty or overly relieved.

The cop dropped his arm and we went inside.

We made our way to our seats, which were in the middle of the row in the middle section of the floor. The auditorium was full to capacity and, except for Nicky and me, there wasn't a white face in the house.

After a few minutes, the lights went down and a wave of rapturous hysteria broke over the crowd. It was show time. The screaming and cheering intensified in volume and pitch when James Brown, Mr. Dynamite himself, took the stage in tight black pants, a black shirt, a checked vest and matching jacket. He counted off and his band, the Famous Flames, launched into "Night Train", immediately electrifying the audience with amplified current.

Right in the middle of the song, he waved his arm for the music to stop. The band went quiet all at once, right on the beat.

Brown gripped the microphone, twirled around to face his backup singers, and yelled, "I'm workin' hard, the Flames are workin' hard, why ain't you workin' hard?"

The crowd cheered even louder than before, as if they had

something to prove.

He spun back around to face the crowd, ready to start his sweat-soaked soul train. But before he did, he noticed Nicky and me right in the center of the crowd. He flashed his huge grin, pointed at us and said, "These boys down here look like two flakes of snow in a coal bin!"

The frenzied screaming of the crowd was mixed with laughter and applause.

"Are you ready for the Night Train?" said James Brown.

The clamor of the crowd gave the answer, and he asked us again.

"I said are you ready for the Night Train?"

There was more affirmative cheering and the 'Hardest Working Man in Show-Business' counted off once more, ripped back into the song, and proved his singular reputation. Midway through the show, when he sang my theme song, "Papa's Got a Brand New Bag," I felt like he was singing it right to me.

Never in my life had I witnessed such a fervent show of emotion and excitement over anything as I did at that concert. The women screamed and cleaved their chests. A hysterical teen girl fainted dead away and had to be dragged through the crowd to safety by police.

Our big sisters shared the half pints of whisky with us that they smuggled inside in their bras. We danced wildly together and yelled ourselves hoarse until the man left the building and the house lights came back up.

Exhausted and euphoric, we glided from the auditorium through the smoke-filled lobby and out onto the sidewalk. The night air chilled the sweat on my skin and made me shiver.

"Save some for me now, Snowflake," said the big sister

on my arm, laughing, as I handed out more joints to parry the hoots and ridiculous slurs from the men in the crowd, whose Sunday shoes were now dull and their neckties dangled in sweaty knots.

"Was he talking about us when he said that thing about the snowflakes in the coal bin?" asked Nicky, as we shuffled back to Bert's car.

"Are you kidding me?" I said. "Who else would he have been talking about?"

4 - LEAVING ON A JET PLANE

In the summer of 1966, I went to visit Johnny and Bobby in the Panama Canal Zone the week before they were to come to Georgia to visit their grandmother. As a friend of the family, I was able to fly to Panama and back courtesy of the United States Navy. I met Johnny and Bobby's friends, who were all kids from the American school. There had even been a rock band in Johnny and Bobby's neighborhood, but they had just lost their drummer when his father went to Viet Nam and he moved back to South Dakota with his mom. Mostly, the kids that I met were as comfortable and ordinary as the ones in the subdivisions back home. I also met Jorge Garcia, a friend who shaped the course of my future.

Jorge's mother was an accountant and a civilian contractor for the U.S. government. This allowed Jorge, who was Panamanian, to attend the American school where he was good friends with Johnny and Bobby. He was a fat and friendly with curly black hair. He invited Johnny, Bobby, and me to dinner at his house one night.

Heat and the smell of grilling beef and onions spread from the kitchen and filled the house. It carried to the back patio where we ate along with Jorge's little brothers and sisters at a long table. Jorge's mother was as short and round as he was and seemed to have limitless tolerance for the noise of children. Rather, she seemed to gather energy from it. With a wide smile, she talked to each child and teenager at the table, drawing us all together. She asked us questions about ourselves, and encouraged us to eat more, insisting that we take second and third helpings of the rich and plentiful food.

After dinner, I was so full that I didn't want to move,

but Jorge suggested we go to his cousin's house a few miles east of the Naval base. As the sun set, Jorge, Johnny, Bobby, and I got into an old Ford Galaxy and rode into the warm, unfolding night.

Jorge's cousin was in his mid-twenties and a completely different type of guy than Jorge. He was reticent and lean and had a sparse mustache. An indistinct tattoo showed under the sleeve of his sweaty t-shirt.

We sat around the tiny, undecorated living room and listened to the radio for a while with nobody saying much of anything. I was beginning to wonder why we had come when Jorge and his cousin started speaking to one another in Spanish. Eventually, his cousin rose, stubbed out his cigarette, and said, "*Vamanos*."

"*Vamanos*," repeated Jorge and Johnny, Bobby, and I followed his cousin through the kitchen, down the back stairs, and out to a padlocked garage that stood separate from the house. Inside, under tarps, practically filling the back half of the little garage, were stacks and stacks of compressed kilos of Panama Red, the same weed that I sold on Big Nine. Jorge turned to me and grinned.

He and his cousin spoke in Spanish some more. After their conversation, his cousin warmed up to me and finally introduced himself as Ramon.

The next day, Johnny, Bobby and I piled into the back of Ramon's pickup truck, and he drove us, with Jorge riding shotgun out to a remote acreage of Panamanian badlands. He stopped the truck, and we hiked across a hot field of tall, sharp grass. I thought maybe there was a lake out there that I couldn't see; maybe we were going swimming. Sweating and breathing hard, we crested a hill. In the valley below was a huge field of tall marijuana plants - the source.

We stood silently for the moment looking wordlessly from one another to the field below. At once, as if signaled by a starting pistol that only we heard, we charged down the hill. The plants were six and seven feet tall with thin, dark green leaves and hairy, orange and red buds.

We stripped off our shirts and ran, arms outstretched, through the field. Our astonished laughter rang out when we could no longer see one another in the redolent field. A breeze cut through valley, the first one all day.

When we regrouped, my skin was itchy from the tiny cuts made by the saw-toothed leaves and sharp stalks. We were all covered in crystals and hairs from the ripe buds. Ramon opened his pocketknife and showed us how to scrape the keif off our skin and collect it. He took a pipe out of his shirt pocket and loaded it with what we had scraped off our arms and chests, and we smoked it sitting on the tailgate of the truck.

The rest of the week Johnny, Bobby, Jorge, and I smoked pot and played a version of baseball and performed, while trying not to be obvious about it, for the cute Panamanian girls who were trying not be obvious about noticing us. We ate dinner at Jorge's house two more times before it was time to go back to the States and each time his mother was as hospitable and tolerant of our boisterous energy as she had first been.

When it was time to fly back to the States, Johnny, Bobby and I all had duffle bags full of weed. I was nervous as we handed them to a young guy in a Navy uniform. Johnny assured me that everything was cool, and we watched the guy toss our duffle bags on top of the suitcases and other cargo they were flying to the U.S. Johnny and Bobby's dad was a Lieutenant Commander, a rank high that was enough to create a vacuum of oversight. Nobody asked to examine Lt. Cdr. Helton's bags or those of his friends.

At the Hartsfield-Jackson International Airport in Atlanta, another young guy in a Navy uniform off-loaded our bags. Between Johnny and Bobby and me, we had just smuggled ninety kilos of weed into the United States on Uncle Sam's dime.

I started going to Panama and coming back with Johnny and Bobby for their twice yearly visits to Georgia. Throughout high school, we imported 400 pounds of weed a year like that. Almost all of it ended up in Diamond matchboxes being passed from hand to hand on Big Nine.

5 - IN-A-GADDA-DA-VIDA

By 1967 and the Summer of Love, the number of garage bands in the subdivisions had swollen to eight. Society Inc. changed their name to The Lively Set and then Aura, but they still didn't buy more than a couple of nickel bags a week. That was pretty typical of the other bands too. Compared to Big Nine, the subdivisions were a lot of legwork for little money, but the Profit brothers, Kevin, Andrew, and Ronnie, got new Schwinn Orange Crate bikes for Christmas and were happy to make the rounds.

Ronnie, the youngest, had particular flair for the role, combining traits of the traveling salesman and the secret agent. There never was a more low-key ten year old. He would sell three or four bags a week while Andrew and Kevin would only sell two or three between them.

Of the three brothers, Ronnie was the one that I developed the closest bond with. In spite of his young age, he had a serious mind and was more focused than his older brothers. One evening in the back of the barn, I was giving Ronnie a handful of nickel bags to sell and we made a pledge: "let us be friends as long we want and never want as long as we're friends." We shook on it and he rode his shiny, new Orange Crate back home.

Nicky and I were still making our deliveries to Big Nine on Thursday nights. There, I could sell 50 or 60 bags a week and it only took an hour or so. We would leave in the late afternoon and be home in time for dinner having just out-earned our fathers.

That fall, Johnny started college at the University of Georgia and moved to Athens. When he did, our weed business took a hit, due to his missing weight, but it was barely noticeable. I still flew to Panama and back with Bobby twice a year. When I took these trips to Panama, I would try to speak Spanish. Later, I took it in high school, but that study was not like the somewhat slang version that I heard in Panama. In the winter, I would bring a Christmas present to Jorge's mom: dishtowels or a picture frame, something like that. I would get embarrassed when she opened it and said how much she loved it.

Back home, I was the starting quarterback of our high school football team, the Valley Eagles. After one particularly brutal beating we gave our rivals, Lakeview-Fort Oglethorpe, in the fall of 1968, coach Ron Henderson was quoted in the school paper saying about me, "That boy has more guts than you can hang in a meat house. He's got a real future." I always appreciated that. He was right, I did, and everybody knew it. Taking a risk meant nothing to me. I did it every day.

From the ball fields and hallways to various lover's lanes and matinees around town, high school was a playground for me. Beside my sovereign position on the football team, I had money, I had a car, and I didn't have a curfew. Whatever I wanted, I knew I could get. What I wanted wasn't too complicated. It amounted to conquest- of girls, rivals, and social dynamics.

The other public high schools in the area were about as big as mine, with graduating classes with as many as 350 students. Taken altogether, there was a seemingly endless supply of girls to take out. I dated girls from my school and three other schools as well. My junior year, I went to three different proms. In three weeks of dinners, dances, and parties, I was the only guy who owned his tuxedo.

In 1968 and '69, the shockwaves erupting all over the world, from Southeast Asia to San Francisco and Paris to Chicago, had even reached rural north Georgia. Of all the fallout, nothing affected my peers and me more than the arrival of The Pill.

And when The Pill came to town, the parties in the subdivisions took on a new dimension. Sometimes there were two parties a weekend. Psychedelics and birth control accelerated the typical surge of hormonal teenage adrenaline. We were possessed by a manic drive to experience anything other than nervous, housebound virginity we had known. Sex became a kind of sport and everybody won, at least in my crowd.

My friends and I, first-string football players and big wheels in student government, wanted to know what girls were on The Pill. Those were the girls we wanted to take out because all the major questions and concerns were immediately and favorably resolved. We just took the girls at their word, even a rumor would suffice. If I took out a girl who was on The Pill and wearing pantyhose, that was like hitting the jackpot. Pantyhose were quick and easy get off, and not having to struggle with condoms and garters and all that stuff was very liberating.

Dating became a lot more fun, and I got in trouble a lot more often. With embarrassing frequency, throughout my sophomore, junior, and senior years, I got caught having sex by my parents, my grandfather, Effie (a bunch of times), and by two different teachers at school. By the time I graduated, I had had sex with almost thirty different girls from schools in Tennessee, Georgia, and Alabama.

By then, in addition to garage bands and teen orgies, each subdivision could also claim a Vietnam casualty. There was a lot to distract a young person running at the edge of the future. Even so, I finished high school Student Body President, Homecoming King, and a triple letter man with a solid B average.

I was accepted to the University of Georgia in Athens where Johnny had just finished his sophomore year. In a letter, he wrote me that he was hanging out with a group that liked to "get stoned and fuck for peace." That was good enough for me.

6 - GEORGIA ON MY MIND

A month after my high school graduation, I went to Panama and came back with Bobby and 220 more pounds of Panama Red. When I headed off to college in the fall of 1969, I took it all with me in the trunk of my 1963 Chevy Impala. It had a big trunk and the one hundred kilos filled it up.

Once I got to the University of Georgia campus in Athens, I found my dorm and dropped off my bags. Students living in the dorms weren't allowed to have cars on campus, especially not ones full of weed, and I was trying to figure out what to do with mine. Given its precious cargo, I had to keep it somewhere safe and accessible.

I met Johnny at his fraternity house, which was off-campus, close to the river. He said I could park the car out front until I found a better place, but he didn't seem crazy about the idea. He also didn't seem overjoyed to see me. I didn't expect a brass band, but his chilly, aloof attitude made me think he was posturing to make sure I was aware of his status as a fraternity man. Other than that, he was the same old Johnny. For my part, maybe I could have acted more impressed, but I had other things on my mind.

A few days before classes started, I talked to the owner of a gas station that was close to campus and my dorm. I told the guy that I was a freshman and had just moved into the dorms and needed a place to keep my car. He gave me a suspicious look, and I explained that the University forbade dorm students from cluttering up the campus with a bunch of parked cars.

He nodded as if he already knew that. I told him that I

really loved my car, and that his gas station looked the cleanest and most secure of all the ones I had considered, and that I knew I could trust the owner of such a fine establishment. That softened him, and then when I offered him twenty bucks a week for basically nothing, he said yes.

My first class in the morning of the first day of classes was Accounting 101. It met in a classroom the size of an auditorium. I sat in the middle looking around at all the strange new faces, unable to totally focus on the far away professor who was going over the syllabus in a sleepy, monotonous voice. I was amazed when out of the crowd of forward-facing students I spotted someone I knew from back home. It was a guy named Larry. He was a senior at the Valley High when I was in the eighth grade. He had brothers closer to my age, and I had watched him play football, which was how I recognized him.

I caught up with him after class and reintroduced myself. He remembered me immediately and seemed as relieved as I was to see a familiar face. We each had a couple of hours before our next class, and he invited me over to his house to catch up. He had married a girl from the Valley named May, and they lived less than a mile from campus.

May worked as a teller at a bank, and he said we would have the place to ourselves.

After he graduated, Larry joined the Navy and, having just completed his four-year enlistment, was going to college on the G.I. Bill. So, despite our age difference, he was a freshman too. Larry lived in a modern, three bedroom brick house with a detached 2 car garage in a new subdivision. We went inside, crashed in front of his second-hand coffee table, and he rolled a joint. We got high and shot the breeze about the Valley, his brothers, football, and our mutual acquaintances.

It wasn't even noon, but he offered me a beer, and I took it.

Feeling relaxed and subconsciously eager to impress Larry, with whom I was suddenly, it seemed to me, on more or less equal footing, I told him about the 220 pounds of weed I had in the trunk of my car, and the predicament I was in as far as finding a place to stash it.

"There's plenty of room here," he said.

"Really?" I said, "May won't mind?"

"Nah, she's cool. She got a great deal on the mortgage, working at the bank: $480 a month which includes, insurance and tax. But we're still broke."

"Well, if you need some extra income I think I have a proposition for you." Larry was all ears. "I'll rent out your garage to store the weed. Your place is so close to campus that I can keep my car in there too. Does $200 a month sound good to you?"

Larry grinned, we got some cold beers out of the fridge and toasted on it, and then he drove us both back to campus.

A day or two later, Larry and I went to Sears and I bought a variable temperature freezer with a lock on it. It was plenty big for the intended task. I had it delivered the same day. I paid Larry two hundred dollars for storing the weed in the freezer. The deal worked out great for both of us as the money covered nearly half his mortgage.

By December and the end of my first quarter, I had sold exactly one kilo of pot on campus. No longer able to make my regular trips to Panama, I knew I had to make the remaining 99 kilos last as long as I could. The weed was already completely dried out and the freezer was preserving the quality while I took my time selling the rest of it.

I would swing by Larry and May's place and get 2 kilos out of the freezer. In the garage, I would take a hand saw and cut one kilo in half. Even with the stems, each half was a little more than a pound. Then I would break the other kilo into 35 individual ounces. I did all of this on top of the freezer using hand scales. When I had everything weighed out, I would take it all to campus and start selling. The fraternities were easily the biggest market. I was selling an average of two pounds a week to those guys.

My original plan had been to join Johnny's fraternity, but we discussed it and he made a good case for my joining one of the fraternities on Lumpkin Street, which ran along the opposite side of campus. That way, we were likely to meet more people and thereby broaden our customer base. So, I joined a fraternity on Lumpkin Street, and, in the spring of 1970, I moved out of the dorm and into the fraternity house.

The fraternity was a big one and the house was a ton of fun. The other guys and I spent a lot of time after class sitting around listening to records and smoking cigarettes. Working in the house was a full-time cook named Julia and a busboy who went by Coot. They were both middle-aged, but Coot looked a lot older because he was a functioning alcoholic and a heavy smoker. There was also an assistant named Belle who was in her early twenties and must have weighed a conservative 350 pounds.

The fraternity, one of the biggest on the Lumpkin Street side of campus, was well-funded with an extensive budget for keg parties and mixers with live bands. All of the guys liked to drink, but quite a few of them were anti-pot and any other form of "hippie bullshit." While none of us were actually hippies, I naturally gravitated toward to the pro-pot clique within the fraternity. Cliquishness was a typical aspect of fraternity life and every house had a its drug and booze factions, but we still considered ourselves to be brothers in spite of our differences.

Shortly after I moved into the house, I bought a used 1957 Harley-Davidson Sportster. I did not want to take chances driving the 63' Chevy around. A Harley was easier, and I loved the freedom of driving a motorcycle. Riding around campus one bright blue April day, I saw a big tent set up on the lawn of the Student Union. In front of that was a card table manned by five girls, decked out in the typical female variety of "hippie bullshit:" flimsy sundresses, halter-tops, sandals, beads, granny glasses, and long braided hair.

My interest was piqued and I pulled a tight U-turn and cut the engine on the opposite side of the street.

"What's going on?" I asked and nodded toward the tent.

"It's Earth Day," one of them said and gave a wide chemically-enhanced smile.

"What the hell is Earth Day?" I asked. I had never heard of it.

Talking in turn, they explained it to me. How it was a newly declared day for celebrating Mother Earth and raising "ecological consciousness." These were no sorority girls. They had clearly done their homework and were obviously deeply committed to their environmental cause. They were clever and totally lacking in the self-righteous pretension that made most social-justice-type hippies such a drag.

Two of them were Music majors, one was studying Political Science, another was working on a double major - Psychology and Philosophy, and another was majoring in P.E. If I had to guess, I would have said that one was a lesbian, but she was no less charming for it, and she had a great body. Despite their variety of coursework, they were activists they said, radicals. I could tell they weren't just playing the part either; these girls embodied the true hippy spirit.

Eventually, we moved on from consciousness-raising to more general get-to-know-you stuff. They told me how they had prepped together at a girls' school in Woodstock, Georgia, and how they had backpacked through Europe by themselves after their junior year of high school. When they graduated, one of girls' fathers, who owned a successful lumberyard, had bought her a Volkswagen bus which they drove to Woodstock, the legendary music festival.

"The girls from Woodstock went to Woodstock!" one of the Music majors said, and we all laughed.

I tried to play it cool, but I was impressed.

After a few more minutes of chitchat, one of the girls, the Psychology and Philosophy double major, whose name was Sarah, said she needed to leave to go get a book. I volunteered to give her a ride on my Harley and she eagerly accepted. The other girls talked to Sarah in a foreign language, and before we got onto the bike I said, "What was that all about?"

"We speak Latin." That's all she said.

All five of the girls lived together in a small, nondescript house with a small lawn full of weeds. Inside, the place looked empty and messy at the same time.

"I'll just be a second," said Sarah going down the hall for her book. "Make yourself at home."

There was no chance of that, so I just stood there looking around. What furniture they had looked salvaged and make-shift. A large wooden, utility company cable spool turned on its side was being used as a table. It had a diameter of about eight feet and on top were empty wine bottles and beer cans and an ashtray piled with cigarette butts and roaches, the marijuana kind. There were probably some real roaches crawling around there too.

Sarah came back in the living room with her book. "Okay, let's go," she said.

"Back to the Student Union?" I said.

She shrugged, "Anywhere. I still have some time before class.

Where do you live?"

"I'll show you," I said and we went outside, got back on the bike and took off for Lumpkin Street.

On the way to my fraternity house, we passed a deserted, antebellum mansion with a "House For Rent" sign in one of the windows.

"Let's check it out," shouted Sarah above the engine noise of the Harley.

I pulled over and we went up the crumbling, stone steps that led to the warped, front porch that ran the length of the house. We shielded our eyes with our hands to block out the reflection as we looked in the windows. It was dark inside, but I could tell that just enough renovations had been done to the place to bring it up to the threshold of livability. We walked around the property and looked in every window we could reach. The rooms were huge with high ceilings. There were ornate structural details that made me think the house was built before the turn of the century. It had what you would call "character" and I loved the look of it. Sarah agreed that it was incredible, but a little run down.

A week later, I met with the old woman who owned the place and signed a four year lease. By the end of the quarter, I had moved out of the fraternity house, and by June 1st was living in the old mansion at the far end of Milledge Avenue with all five of the girls from Woodstock. Even with six of us in there, we still had plenty of room to spare.

Sarah, Cindy (Phys Ed), Linda (Poli Sci), Sharon and Sandy (Music) brought with them guitars, flutes, incense, a striped cat named Tabby Hoffman, bongos, wind chimes, and all sorts of other counterculture accessories. In no time at all, the place was decked out in such a way as to give any Victorian flop house this side of
Haight-Ashbury a run for its dirty money.

The girls were constantly bringing home flowers and draping tie-dyed tapestries over things. Every doorway was hung with colorful beads. Black light posters and psychedelic show bills for bands like the Jimi Hendrix Experience and Jefferson Airplane covered the walls. The place reeked of Black Love incense and patchouli oil.

A friend of mine from Macon, Georgia named Mike moved in.

His hippie credibility rested on the fact that he had smoked pot and taken mushrooms a bunch of times with the Allman Brothers. Another guy named Bob also moved in at the same time. At twenty-four years old, he was the oldest guy in the house. He had been selling insurance in Atlanta, and once he had saved enough money to buy a car and pay for tuition, he enrolled at UGA to get in on all the sex, drugs, and rock n' roll that he'd been hearing about. I don't know how he found his way to us, but there he was. More than anything else, the common denominator among all eight of us in the house was marijuana. We all loved to get stoned.

At night, when everybody was finished studying, we would gather around the giant cable spool that the girls had brought over from their old place. It had been refurbished in keeping with the wild style of our new digs. The girls, who were far more creative and industrious than any of the guys in the house, had sanded it, painted it and covered it with stickers that they then lacquered over. We had eight bar stools, one for each of us, and we would sit around the spool-table and eat dinner together. Afterward, the girls would play their guitars and bongo drums and sing.

If the girls wanted to say something private to one another without whispering, they would speak Latin. After a few months of being left out of the conversation, I learned it too. I had already learned German in elementary school and Spanish in high school. Latin wasn't that hard to pick up. Speaking a dead language only added to our fun.

Sarah was the first girl that I ever knew who had a tattoo. It was of a rose on her forearm. In 1970, it was extremely rare for a woman to have a tattoo, but for a college-age young woman it was just not done. There weren't even that many guys who had tattoos, and for the most part the ones that did had been to Vietnam or prison, or they were in a biker gang. The Woodstock Five, as the girls became known, were my introduction to a truly freewheeling lifestyle. It was an eye opener, to say the least.

More than once, I woke up to find that one the girls had gotten into bed with me. They would say they were bored or lonely or just wanted to ball. Sometimes, they wouldn't give any explanation. A naked girl who took the pill and climbed in my bed, was its own explanation and I never protested the intrusion. I just went along with whatever they wanted to do. Sometimes, Mike or Bob ended up with one of the girls in his bed, and they took a similarly obliging attitude. Getting laid, which had never really been a problem, would never be as uncomplicated again.

I was on the so-called "five-year-plan" at UGA, and this was pretty much the way life rolled along with my roommates for the next four years. It was just great. In all that time, I didn't go home to the Valley very often. Why would I? Athens, and my rented mansion, had everything I wanted and needed to keep me stoned, happy and busy.

Midway through our first summer in the house, it was obvious that we were going to have to do something to stay cool. We left the windows open and ran fans constantly, but all that did was stir the hot air. It was absolutely sweltering upstairs where the bedrooms were. We bought individual air-conditioning units and put them in all the bedroom windows. The Music majors, Sandy and Sharon, shared a bedroom, but everybody else had their own room with their own AC unit. I even had my own bathroom. It was one of four in the house.

The back yard, where the girls would sunbathe in the nude, was huge. It had a tall privacy fence around it, not that it mattered to the girls as they were into Free Love and not at all hung up about stuff like casual nudity or causing stares. They didn't shave, but they did occasionally shower. They were very free and open about themselves.

One afternoon at the beginning of July, I noticed the girls taking duffle bags, blankets, the ubiquitous acoustic guitars, and a bunch of other stuff out of the house and loading it all into the bus, which was parked on the street out front. I went out on the porch and asked them where they were going. They told me they were going to the Atlanta International Pop Festival which was happening over the Independence Day weekend. They didn't have tickets, but they were sure that they'd get in once they were there, just like it had happened at Woodstock.

I said, "If it's as simple as that, I want to go."

There was some eye-rolling, hemming and hawing,

and Latin thrown around. They said they wanted to "do their own thing" and didn't want to have to deal with any "hang ups" or "male ego trips."

I was doggedly persistent, which is one of my greatest strengths, and eventually they acquiesced on the condition that I pitch in some drug money. That made me laugh.

"Sure," I said. "No problem. Let me get some stuff together and then stop by my friend Larry's place."

I still had about a hundred pounds of pot in the freezer over there. When I dropped that choice little bombshell, they were suddenly more than happy to have me along, ego and all.

Atlanta International Pop Festival was something of a misnomer as the festival actually happened in Byron, Georgia, which is about ninety miles southeast of Atlanta. The lineup included The Allman Brothers, Grand Funk Railroad, Mountain, Ten Years After, and Jimi Hendrix. We got to the festival site a day early and were directed to park in a wide, open, grassy field that sloped gently down to a six or seven acre lake in the middle of it. We parked the bus under the shade of a tree at the edge of the lake. Even there in the shade, the heat was stifling.

That night we lay down to sleep on the ground trying to catch any kind of breeze that might blow. None did.

Between the heat and the excitement of all the people that were arriving and parking, filling up the field throughout the night, it was impossible to sleep. In the afternoon, we made our way to the gate. By that time, a quarter of a million hippies, Yippies, freaks, bikers, and other counterculture mutants had shown up. The seven-foot-high cyclone fence that encircled the festival grounds collapsed with no more resistance than dried weeds under the devil's own purple smoke-belching threshing machine. It was pressed into the earth under a confused and brutal stampede of Jerusalem jumpers and, summarily, the fence was forgotten. The Woodstock Five had predicted this turn of events and, swept away by the sweaty, bearded, free-loving, freak-powered throng, we went on in.

Not to put too fine a point on it, the first of the festival, passed in a blur. I have only a vague recollection of hair, body odor, guitar solos, seemingly interminable drum solos, and marijuana smoke which hung over the crowd all day and night in the thick, humid air. My head was spinning and, all of a sudden, it was dark, and just as suddenly we were back at the bus. I don't know how we got there. Obviously, we walked, but exactly how we found our way is a mystery. I passed out on top of a sleeping bag that the girls had unrolled. They were prepared and sober enough to take care of necessities. Lucky me.

In the morning, I turned on the radio in the bus just in time to hear a weather forecast of sun and an afternoon high of more than a hundred degrees. At ten in the morning, it was already in the upper eighties. The girls and I, and three hundred other hippies took towels and bars of soap down to the lake, stripped naked and jumped in.

That afternoon, the heat was so oppressive that we didn't have energy for much more than sitting around, dozing, drinking cheap wine, and getting stoned. When the shadows got long in the late afternoon, a merciful breeze swept over the field and with it a wave of excitement slowly started to build. The girls and I decided to weave through the field and see what all our new brothers and sisters were doing.

Throughout the vast field, people had set up card tables and spread blankets on which they openly displayed all manner of illegal, mind-altering substances. Much like the itinerant hucksters and snake oil salesmen of days gone by, they barked out their exotic inventories: Grass! Peyote! Psilocybin! Mescaline! Not only was there LSD, but buyers had their choice of Window Pane, Blue Cheer or Orange Sunshine.

Also for sale in the open-air drug bazaar was every type of paraphernalia required to smoke, snort, shoot, and otherwise ingest the chemicals as efficiently as possible into the brain and nervous system. For just a few dollars, there was no excuse for not staggering around like an incoherent, drooling monster with pupils like either pie plates or pinholes, depending on your choice of exit ramp on the expressway to instant nirvana. The girls were laughing and having a good time.

We walked all the way to the far edge of the field and a few blocks down the road on which we had originally arrived. There was a convenience store with a noisy, complaining crowd milling around in the parking lot. We were about to turn around and go back to the bus, but decided to see what the commotion was instead.

A burly Hell's Angel had parked his filthy hog across the entrance to the store and was waving a buck knife and shaking down anybody that tried to come in or out. Nobody could get past him unless they paid a tax of money, food, or drugs, which was about all anybody had of any value. The crowd around the store was about two hundred deep and this one Angel was commanding them all easily and clearly enjoying his blackshirt authority.

Such thuggery was generally anathema to the hippie mindset, but so was being cut to ribbons by a sadist over a pack of cigarettes or a roll of toilet paper. For whatever reason, call it Flower Power, this particular group was incapable of realizing the strength of their number, disarming the punk, and restoring democracy.

The Angel was easily six and a half feet tall and weighed a conservative 230 pounds. In front of me in the crowd was a guy with a Government Issue high-and-tight haircut who was six foot four. In another life I might have made a good living guessing peoples' weights at a carnival, and I put this guy at 210 pounds, all of it muscle. As happens in prisons and jungles where the alpha male protects his status by dominating the next biggest beast, the Angel singled out this guy in front of me for abuse, trying to goad him into a fight.

The Angel got off his bike and started coming our way. When he spotted my grubby little harem and me, he started groping the girls and trying to snatch their bags. They started screaming and, while I was in no mood to get stabbed defending some girls who were always denouncing materialism and the evils of property anyway, my pride wouldn't let me stand by and watch my friends being bullied. My mind was racing for a bloodless solution, but I was coming up empty.

Luckily, I didn't have to sweat it long. The big guy, who had been standing in front of me, quickly reappeared at my right and hit the assailing Angel square on the edge of his jaw. The force of the impact made a sharp cracking sound and dropped the Angel instantly to his knees. Then he pitched face down onto the hot asphalt. A pool of dark blood spread under his unconscious face as the crowd of stunned hippies erupted in grateful cheers and whoops.

Our hero stepped over the vanquished Angel and picked up the buck knife he had dropped and walked coolly over to his motorcycle and cut the tires. With a venomous hiss, the bike sagged and fell over. Again the crowd cheered, but the guy didn't seem to hear it; He dropped the knife and started to go into the store as if nothing had happened.

I had never seen anything like that in my life, and being the great appreciator of personal excellence that I am, I touched the guy's rock hard shoulder to stop him.

He turned and I said, "That was the coolest thing I have ever seen, man. Thank you."

He smiled and nodded and started again to go into the store and again I stopped him.

"Really, man, thanks. What's your name?"

"Dennis," he said and we shook hands.

I introduced the girls and myself. "We've got a bus parked down at the lake and whole bunch of grass. Why don't you join us? Come hang out."

He agreed and we made our way back through the crowd still buzzing with the energy of what we had all seen. At the bus, we began to unwind. We all ate mushrooms and washed them down with Boone's Farm strawberry wine. Then, we shared joints and got to know one another while waiting for the mushrooms to take effect.

Dennis served in the military and had completed Special Forces training, which is where he developed a profound distaste for bullies and learned to incapacitate them with a single well-aimed punch. He was on leave and staying with his parents in the suburbs outside Atlanta. A couple of days before, he decided to come down to Byron just to check it out. The girls and I, plus two hundred other people at the convenience store, were glad he did.

By sundown, we were tripping hard. At midnight, we watched in psychedelic awe as Jimi Hendrix played "The Star Spangled Banner" with his teeth. When the music ended and the warm hum of feedback receded, a fireworks display thundered and splashed color across the black sky. A full spectrum of stars cascaded again and again from heaven, bathing the ecstatic crowd in a mist of vibrating light. When the booming stopped and sky was once more empty and quiet, we made our way back to the bus. Sarah and I had sex in a sleeping bag while inside the bus, Dennis screwed all four of the other girls, even Cindy the

P.E. major, who was obviously at least bisexual.

On Sunday morning, I woke up early to find Dennis already dressed. He said that he was due to report to Ranger school at Fort Stewart, Georgia in the next couple of days and needed to get moving. We smoked a joint together and laughed that he had gotten quite the send off. I had him write down an address and phone number where I might reach him when he was finished with Ranger school. Then, walking tall, he made his way through the misty field of exhausted and lazily stirring campers and was gone. I had a good feeling about Dennis and I knew I would see him again sometime, somewhere.

When the girls finally woke up, we broke camp. The crowd in the field had thinned out, and just after noon we headed back to Athens. As soon as we got back to our house, I went upstairs to my room and took a long, hot shower and went to sleep.

Monday morning, I got on my bike and went looking for Johnny. He still lived in his fraternity house. In the fall, he was going to be the president of the fraternity and he took the role very seriously. He let me in and went up to his room.

I said, "Look, we need to make a run. Bobby is telling me he wants to go and volunteer for the service because it's only for two years. I've got weed now, but I don't know how that's gonna end."

In August, Johnny and I went to Panama and got with Bobby right before he graduated high school and enlisted in the Army. Then, we all came back, bringing with us a total of 198 pounds (ninety kilos), thirty kilos each. They were the last forty-nine dollar kilos I ever got. When we got back, Bobby stayed in Athens in the fraternity house with Johnny.

I went back to Sears and bought two more freezers. I had

them delivered to Larry's place. That brought the total up to 3 freezers in his garage, all of them full of pot. I stored my weed there in those freezers for the next two and a half to three years.

Sarah and Cindy stayed in the house that summer. The other three girls, Linda, Sharon and Sandy, grudgingly went back to Woodstock, Georgia at the behest of their parents. When they left, they said they would be back as soon as they could.

In the fall, with school starting again, I committed myself to dope dealing and studying, in that order, more or less. I decided to break the kilos up into ounces and take my time unloading them. I had about four guys in fraternities that would take a pound every week to ten days, which was going to empty the freezers quickly enough, and even though I had just decided to slow roll my dealing, I was never one to sit on a good idea once it came to me, especially a moneymaking idea. The price of weed had gone up since the summer, and I had an idea.

The girls were all back in town, and we were settling into a smooth routine in the house. In the late fall and winter, the house was as cold and drafty as it had been hot and stuffy in the summer. There was an old furnace connected to a system of radiators that burned expensive and smelly fuel oil. Between that and half a dozen floor heaters, we managed to stay warm.

One night after dinner, when we were sitting around in wool sweaters getting high, I asked the girls if they wanted to make some easy money. And, of course, they did.

Every day, I would give each girl an ounce of pot. They would break it up into quarters and sell those for ten dollars apiece. I let them keep half the money. Every evening when they got home they'd each hand me twenty bucks and say, "See ya in the morning!"

Between going to class, selling quarter bags, and never

missing a concert or party, the girls founded a National Organization of Women (NOW) chapter on campus. They were totally different than the sorority girls on campus or the girls I had known back home in the Valley, none of whom would have gone to Woodstock or the Atlanta Pop Festival. For these girls, my housemates, that kind of thing was their blackberry bush. They were playful, but also worldly and wise beyond their years. I credit them with giving me a whole new and different perspective on women, the world, and life in general.

By December, I was calling them the Profit Sisters. They wondered why but I never told them about Kevin, Andrew, and Ronnie, the brothers back home in the Valley who had played the roles the girls now occupied.

At the start of the Christmas holiday, I got out my calculator and figured that with the weed I had and at the rate I was selling it, I stood to make 60,000 dollars over the next two years. That certainly put me in the holiday spirit.

7 - WHITE WEDDING

Exactly one year later, during the winter break of 1971, Johnny, Bobby and I made our final trip to Panama. When we got there, we were surprised to discover that the price of weed had doubled. Jorge's price had gone from ten to twenty dollars a kilo, and my price was up to one hundred a kilo.

Everything was changing. With Bobby on leave and awaiting deployment to Vietnam, I knew that this was going to be our last, and most expensive, run. I wanted to make it count.

We flew back together as we had always done with another 220 pounds of Panama Red among us. In the first cold days of 1972, shortly after I got the load over to Athens and locked away in the freezers, Bobby flew to Oakland, California and from there to Viet Nam. I took it for granted that I would see him at least one more time before he shipped off, but I was wrong. I never said goodbye or good luck or anything, and by February, it was too late. He was killed in action.

That June, one of my fraternity brothers was getting married in Dothan, Alabama to the heiress of a peanut fortune. Everyone referred to her as the Peanut Princess of Dothan, and if I ever heard her real name, I immediately forgot it. The wedding was going to be an elaborate affair, and five of my close friends and fraternity brothers were going. They said they wanted ten pounds of weed each. They wanted to take it back home with them to sell over the Summer.

"No way," I said. "There is no way I'm getting rid of that much weed."

But the guys wouldn't shut up about it. They said they would pay the premium price, and given the fact that the price of weed plummets in a college town like Athens in the summertime, I capitulated.

My date for the wedding was a really tall girl named Helen Jane. She was a little sister in my fraternity. She was five foot nine in bare feet, which is tall to me because I'm just an inch taller. In heels, she was even taller than me. She probably weighed 125 pounds and she was good looking.

A day before the wedding, we headed down to Dothan in my Impala. The freeway wasn't completed yet, and we sped down long two-lane country roads singing along with the radio.

We smoked joints, drank beer, and tossed the empty cans out the windows into grassy fields as we went. Helen Jane wasn't really a hippy, and neither was I for that matter, but she knew how to have a good time just the same. The fifty pounds of pot I had agreed to bring was packed in a duffle bag in the trunk.

When we got to Birmingham, it was rush hour. We were stuck in bumper-to-bumper traffic, slowly creeping from red light to red light. With so many people so close to us, we couldn't smoke pot or drink and had no choice but to sit tight.

At one point, two pretty young girls wearing micro mini skirts and high heels walked out of a bank building. Up ahead, the light turned yellow, and I stopped knowing that I would never make it across the crowded intersection. In the rearview mirror, I could see the balding, middle-aged driver of the car behind us rubbernecking in an obvious way to watch the two girls stroll down the sidewalk. He was staring out the window and paying no attention at all to his driving. Helplessly, I watched as he slowly and steadily approached my car, showing no indication of stopping. Then, instinctively, I reached across Helen Jane to brace her for the impact.

When it came, there was a metallic crunching sound and Helen Jane and I jolted forward. He hadn't been going fast enough to hurt us, but the force of the collision was sufficient to pop my trunk right open.

A cold panic seized me immediately. My first thought was of the now exposed duffle bag and the 50 pounds of pot inside it.

"Oh shit," I said. "Holy shit!"

My pulse was pounding, I was sweating, and my mind was spinning. I strained to put together a coherent sequence of thoughts. People were beginning to gather on the sidewalk and stare at the accident.

In a shaking voice that sounded like it was coming over a distant staticky wire, I said to Helen Jane, "The police will be here any minute. We have to get that pot out of the trunk and get rid of it now or we're going to jail."

Helen Jane's eyes widened in disbelief because this had not occurred to her. Her open mouth moved, but no sound came out.

Onlookers were gingerly stepping closer and closer to the car to see if anyone was injured. The guy who hit us was still sitting in his car, dazed.

I looked around frantically for anything to trigger a plan. Three or four blocks in the distance, on the right, I spotted a sign with the Greyhound logo on it - a bus station.

Without thinking, and speaking quickly in the same far away sounding voice, I said, "Get out. Get the duffle bag and take it down there to the bus station. Take the bus to Dothan and I'll pick you up there."

She just sat there wide-eyed and gaping as I scrambled to pull a handful of tens and twenties from my wallet. I forced them into her hand and yelled, "Right now! Go!"

The guy who hit us was out of his car now and looking at the

damage.

Helen Jane snapped to it and jumped out of the car. She went to the trunk, threw the duffel bag over her shoulder and started walking as best she could with the heavy load.

"Hey!" I heard the guy behind me call out to her. "You okay?"

She didn't look back and kept hustling down the sidewalk through the crowd to the Greyhound station.

"Oh man, I'm sorry. I didn't mean to hit you!" said the guy who was now at my window sweating profusely.

With Helen Jane disappeared down the sidewalk, I was beginning to relax. "Yeah, I didn't think you did," I said. "I saw you watching those girls. I knew what was coming."

He forced a chuckle. "Those damn mini skirts are going to kill us, man."

By his choice of the word "us" I knew he was trying to bind us into some sort of camaraderie, which I could understand and even forgive, but I wasn't really in the mood to buddy up to this guy.

"Who was that girl in your car?" he said. "She sure was a big, skinny gal."

"Sure was," I said.

"I'm not saying she wasn't good looking." He forced another dopey sounding chuckle and wiped his face with a handkerchief. "She sure took off in a hurry. She your girlfriend?"

"What?" I said getting annoyed. "No. I don't know who she was. She was a hitchhiker."

The police showed up about that time and took down all our information. Even though I was totally clean, I was still rattled and it took effort not to act nervous. One of the cops helped me tie my trunk down with a length of twine and then I was on my way.

Start to finish, the whole thing took about forty-five minutes, but that didn't matter. I got to the bus station in Dothan just a few minutes before Helen Jane arrived.

I was relieved to see her step off the bus. The driver helped her pull the duffle bag out of the cargo hold. Helen Jane wasn't mad when she got in the car. In fact, she was smiling and seemed to have gotten a kick out of the whole thing. And I had a good story to tell at the wedding.

8 - FOR THE LOVE OF MONEY

Johnny graduated from UGA that summer and took a job with an accounting firm in Atlanta. He had no more interest in going back and forth to Panama anymore. He was focused on his new job and earning a legitimate, taxable income. Since Bobby's death, he had withdrawn, and though I hated to see the end of the gravy train, I didn't try to sway him from a life to which he was committed.

That's how our teenage drug ring spun out. For eight years, I had provided a rare and valuable service to the least discriminating clientele imaginable. I made a lot of money for myself and other people. It was made possible by the unwitting auspices of the U.S. government, which had provided fast, reliable, and free transportation for the weed.

In the spring of 1974, right before I graduated, I went to Atlanta for a week to introduce myself to prospective employers. I also caught up with Johnny. He was exhausted from work and didn't feel like getting high, but he agreed to meet for cocktails.

Our conversation was slow, and he seemed distracted. There were no women in the bar either, just a few tired guys like him. I paid for the round, he got the next one, and then we said goodnight.

That summer, with my newly earned degree in Business Administration, I got a job in Atlanta selling computers. I was a natural salesman, and once again I combined the role with that of explorer and conqueror. I was racking up huge commissions and bonuses selling cutting-edge technology that every business needed. I was making the future accessible. The market was brand new and absolutely limitless.

Computer systems didn't sell themselves quite the way marijuana did, but the basic principles of selling were the same. I didn't see my sales calls as any different than when I approached a rock band in a garage or a surly club owner on Big Nine. Those days had the faded sweetness of a dream.

At night, I ran around with an ambitious group of young professional men who worked hard and lived fast. Some of them were lawyers and bankers, and some were in the computer business like me. We called ourselves the Young Turks, and we insisted on having the best of everything.

We were regulars in all the most expensive and exclusive clubs and bars in Atlanta. At the time, there was a huge influx of foreign capital, and we regularly hosted international clients and investors. We won their business in large part by feeding them drugs and buying them prostitutes.

In Atlanta, in the mid-1970s, cocaine was around, but it was something of a rare bird. The Young Turks considered ourselves a rare breed. We operated on a higher frequency than most people and required pique levels of stimulation at all times in order to keep our minds diamond sharp.

The coke that was available could be had at a cost that made it prohibitive to most work-a-day wage earners, which we were not. The expense, and the inconsistent quality, was not great enough to keep us Young Turks from doing blow constantly.

Displaying our arrogance, we did it casually in our offices during the day. At night, when we went to parties, bars, and strip joints, we did lines in the bathroom stalls. We would spend a thousand dollars a night at a popular strip club called The Limelight. I was so well-liked there that I could go in the back and do lines with the dancers. I knew them all by name.

When Dennis, the guy that stomped the Hell's Angle at the Atlanta International Pop Festival, got out of the service and was back in Atlanta, I gave him a call. We got together at The Limelight one night and I introduced him to the Young Turks.

Dennis looked square in every way. His hair, per military regulation, was still short. He wore a short-sleeved cotton sport shirt in a neutral color and narrow chinos that looked like they had been hanging in his closet for the past ten years and they probably had. The Young Turks, by contrast, sported wide, striped neckties, wild patterned shirts made of smooth synthetic fibers, and flared slacks in garish hues. We mixed patterns and colors the same way we did everything else, with delirious abandon.

One area in which Dennis was totally ahead of the curve was drugs. Back on his home turf, Dennis had many different connections, and he promptly became our go-to coke and weed guy. The coke was still expensive, but it was easier to get and the quality was incredible.

Because he ran his civilian life like a military operation, Dennis was always reliable and punctual. He was also a good communicator, and if there was ever any delay in getting us our drugs, he always let me know.

No matter how late he stayed out mixing it up with the Young Turks, he rose every morning at six a.m. and ran four miles. As much as he could help it, he didn't let anything interfere with his routine.

I realized that I was buying cocaine the way my customers bought computers: eagerly and at an obscene mark-up. I liked coke a lot, so I knew I needed to get on the winning end of the business. I needed to be a dealer. However, finding a connection and a profit margin anything like the one I used to get from weed was proving difficult.

Dennis was a retailer and protective of his connections, which I respected. It would be better for me to find a way into the coke trade on my own.

My attempts to reconnect with Johnny, just on a friendly level, were also coming to nothing. He was hard to reach and, eventually, I just quit trying. The cocktails we had in the spring of 1974 turned out to be last time I ever saw or heard from him. I thought of him occasionally but without curiosity.

In 1978, after a four-year routine of partying hard, making money, and over-paying for coke, I decided to take my talent and the money I had managed to save down to Miami to get involved in the real cocaine traffic. The market for coke was ravenous and predictable. As good as the straight, computer money was, it couldn't match the electric magnetism of drug money.

9 - COCAINE

Tension runs high trying to buy large amounts of drugs in a strange city full of cagey immigrants. A language barrier, a suitcase full of cash, and a creeping coke addiction corrupt every interaction with paranoia.

I looked up a guy I knew named Brad, who had moved to Miami after high school to become a "service industry professional." He worked as a maintenance man at a shabby, outdated hotel called the Royal Palms. He introduced me to the owner of the place, Mr. Gutierrez. We negotiated a deal whereby I could stay at the hotel for thirty percent of the usual rate, to be paid to Gutierrez each week in cash, until I found a cocaine connection.

Every night, I drove to Miami and went to nightclubs in my white Datsun 240Z. I bought the car two years prior in Atlanta. It was low, sleek, and powerful. Two seats and no trunk, it was as suited to cocaine traffic as the '63 Impala had been to hauling bulky bricks of weed.

I was trying to find a good connection. I met plenty of local, low-level dealers who were selling grams and eight balls at the retail price. It beat the retail price in Atlanta, but what I was looking for was more elusive.

After two months of hanging out in dozens of different bars and clubs in Miami, Hialeah, Hollywood, and Fort Lauderdale, I finally met two tough-looking Colombian dudes who said they had some coke. They both had lots of tattoos of Catholic icons and symbols and hair pulled straight back into short ponytails. I never could tell them apart, but it didn't matter. I just knew that one was T.J. and the other was T.K. They called me Gringo.

I ended up doing half a key with them at an outrageous price. I paid 32,000 dollars for a little more than a pound of coke. It was almost all the money I had.

Despite the cost, I was able to make money on it when I took it back up to Atlanta and sold it to the Young Turks and other young white-collar comers. When I got back to Miami, I went to see T.J. and
T.K. again and they gave me a slightly better price on two kilos.

I only had money for one, so they fronted me the other one. I told them I would bring the money back after I sold the two kilos and they seemed to *comprende*. I drove to Atlanta, sold both kilos, and came back to Miami.

When I got back, I went to a bar and called T.J. and T.K. from a payphone. I had been gone about a week.

"*Donde estas*, Gringo?"

I told whichever one I was talking to where I was and he said, "Good, we don't have to go to Atlanta to kill you."

"Kill me?" I said, "What are you talking about?"

"You stole from us."

"No I didn't," I said, "Look, I've got the money now. That's why I'm calling you."

"It's too late, Gringo. *Estas muerto*," he said and hung up.

I was sitting at the bar confused, trying to gauge the severity of the situation. I reasoned that as soon as they saw the money, that would settle everything, and I tried to relax. When they showed up, they were all frowns. They said their boss wanted to see me.

"*Vamanos*," one of them said.

We went out in the parking lot and I got the cash out of the 240Z. The money was in a blue gym bag. I pulled it from the passenger side and we got in their car, a primer grey two-door Buick. I was sitting in the back and passed the gym bag to them, they unzipped it and looked inside.

"That's 64,000 for the kilo you fronted me, and 120,000 for two more," I said.

T.J. or T.K. said, "Where have you been?"

"I told you. Atlanta. I had to go all the way there and sell all that shit myself."

"*Estas muerto*, Gringo," said the driver turning the key. The Buick started with a rattle and we drove into the heavy, damp night.

Trapped in the backseat, I thought, "They've taken all my money; what good am I now? If they kill me, they can give their boss the money that I owed him and not tell him about the other 120,000. They could split it between them." I was sure T.J. and T.K. were thinking the same thing.

On a residential street lined with tired palm trees and lit by pale green street lights, we pulled into the driveway of a flat, stucco ranch house. A cyclone fence bordered the front yard and bars covered the windows.

T.J. and T.K. had exchanged a couple of quiet remarks in Spanish during the ride over, but I hadn't been able to make any of it out. I assumed I was being led inside to my death and I still didn't know why. Even as a boy on Big Nine, I had been protected by my whiteness and my connections. As a man in Miami, none of that mattered anymore.

They led me inside and motioned for me to sit on the

couch in the living room. While either T.J. or T.K. stood and glared at me, the other one disappeared down the hall. Still, neither one of them said anything. Without my money, I had nothing to leverage for my life, and I was expecting to die in that lousy stucco house.

From down the hall, I heard a door open and the murmur of Spanish voices. A surge of hot fear ran through my limbs and up the back of my neck. My senses were amplified and raw. Time stretched out as the approaching voices grew louder. I felt lightheaded.

When the men entered the living room, I sat up and turned.

What I saw stunned me mute. The boss that wanted to see me was Jorge Garcia.

After a moment of shocked disbelief, we both started laughing at once. I laughed until tears came to my eyes. My knees were shaking as I stood and embraced my old Panamanian friend and boyhood weed connection.

T.J. and T.K. looked confused far into Jorge's explanation of how he and I knew each other. Then, Jorge emptied a huge pile of coke out onto a mirror on the coffee table, and we blew two huge rails. He opened a bottle of tequila and we toasted. Along with the liquor and the cocaine, gratitude flooded my system. I smiled until my face hurt. My appreciation for being alive and being high changed that night completely and forever.

Jorge had left Panama for Miami years ago to protect himself and his money from the unpredictable and corrupt Panamanian government. Our reunion came at a good time for me given my deteriorating relationship with my Colombian buddies, T.K. and T.J. From that point on, I sidestepped them and dealt directly with Jorge. That's when I really got rolling.

My price went from 64,000 dollars a kilo to 36,000. I started paying 1,000 dollars an ounce and selling them for 2,000 dollars in Atlanta. I could double my money without ever touching the dope, without even taking it out of the wrapper. After a few months, I didn't have to drive to Atlanta anymore either.

I called up Dennis and told him I had a job for him. I had him drive down to Miami and pick up a couple of kilos. He drove the coke back up to Atlanta and broke the kilos into quarter pounds, half pounds, and ounces. He delivered those to dealers he knew who were waiting in different cities in Ohio, Kentucky, North Carolina, and Tennessee. The last leg of his route was bringing my money back down to Miami. From start to finish, that routine took about four weeks. It was like having a magic machine that doubled money every month.

In 1981, my price dropped again to 24,000 dollars a key. I moved to an expensive condo in a complex called Seagate Villa in Fort Lauderdale. My days there were lazy in the extreme; I had too much time on my hands.

Every day, I slept until about two o'clock in the afternoon. I would shower and go to a restaurant to eat breakfast at four. Back at my apartment, I smoked pot, drank tequila, and watched TV. And when it got dark, I would start doing coke.

10 - WITCHY WOMAN

I had a state-of-the-art Aiwa M-501 mini component sound system in my condo with an Optonica dual cassette deck and Infinity Reference Standard II speakers. I got it all below wholesale from a twitchy
middle-aged biker with a swastika tattooed on his neck who was fencing it for money to buy speed. I had two tapes of the song "In the Air Tonight" by Phil Collins. I used to play one while the other was rewinding, so I could hear it over and over again. It was great music for sharpening the edge. Once I was tuned up, I drove to Miami at top speed to hit the clubs and bars.

In 1983, I sold the 240Z and bought a black Mercedes-Benz 450SL two-door coupe. I had fancy new wheels, but my routine remained the same. I went to clubs, bars, strip joints, and parties every night. In the pastel dawn, I would drive back to my condo in Fort Lauderdale, most times with a woman I had just met.

Huge amounts of money and cocaine attract a certain spirited class of woman. Sex was more a matter of manic endurance than it had been in the exploratory backseat days of Panama Red, The Pill, and pantyhose. Nevertheless, easy sex was one of the cheap thrills with which I tried to fill my empty days. As my cocaine use increased, even sex became an alienated, meaningless experience.

By the bed with the condoms, I kept an economy-sized bottle of NyQuil that I would chug in an effort to knock myself out after having spent the past seven hours doing high-grade cocaine. The visceral novelty of the lifestyle to which I had succumbed inevitably expired. It left me numb, isolated, and badly addicted.

Now and then I would think, "I gotta get away from this shit." Then I would chase the feeling away by getting high. And anyway, in Miami you don't get away from that shit, especially not when it's 9,000 dollars a key, which is what I was paying. It's what I did for a living; it was my business and business was booming.

Seagate Villa was a horseshoe shaped complex, with the open side facing the ocean. Every condo had a balcony and an ocean view, more or less, which was reflected in the price. The complex mainly catered to young, moneyed, and single white-collar professionals. In the center was a courtyard, an outdoor gym, and a large kidney-shaped swimming pool.

In the evenings, I would sit on my balcony and have a cigarette and cocktail or two before snorting coke and going out for the night.

From across the recreation area below, I started noticing a girl who would sit on her balcony, which was lined up on the same floor as mine on the opposite side of the complex.

She had dirty blonde hair that hung to the middle of her back and golden tan skin. She had a style fairly typical of all the other pretty, young women who hung around at the beach. She mostly wore t-shirts, bikini bottoms and flip-flops. That's what she was always wearing when I would see her on her balcony in the evenings smoking cigarettes and drinking beer from a can, sometimes alone, sometimes with friends.

Occasionally, I would see her out there drinking beer in the middle of the afternoon, and even from a distance it was clear from her body language that she was just starting the day with a little hair of the dog.

I surmised that our schedules were equally flexible, that her time was as cheap as mine. Figuring we probably had more than few things in common, I decided to try to cross paths with her whenever the opportunity presented itself.

I didn't have to wait long, and all my assumptions were proven correct. One night, freshly showered, coked up and feeling invincible, I ran into her in the parking garage under the complex. I was getting into my black 450SL and I spotted her a few spaces away getting into a red 450SL.

"Hey. You've got good taste," I called out.

She turned and looked me up and down. "Hey, so do you."

I resisted the urge to walk over to her.

"I've seen you around," I said. "What's your name?"

"Jane," she said with a smile in her voice and got behind the

wheel.

"Drive safe," I said as she backed out.

She waved and pulled out of the garage.

I watched her go and then got in my car. When I started the engine, "Burning Up" by Madonna was on the radio.

I cranked the volume and punched the gas on the highway to

Miami.

It was a couple of days later before I designed to bump into Jane again in the parking garage.

"I'm curious," I said, "I live across the courtyard from you.

We're on the same floor. I've seen you on the balcony."

"Oh yeah?" she said pleasantly, but with little interest as she unlocked her car. She had a toned, compact body and couldn't have been taller than five feet.

"Yeah," I said. "Looks like we have pretty similar schedules.

What do you do?" I wished I had thought of something more creative to say, but she was on the move, and I wanted her to slow down and give me a minute.

"That's none of your business." She smiled when she said it.

I smiled too, as if it was no big deal either way. "Wow. Well, whatever it is, it obviously requires lots of charm and wit."

"I'm sure." She laughed and rolled her ice blue eyes.

"Come have a drink with me."

"Okay. Some other time though. I'm busy tonight," she said and backed out of her space.

A few nights after that, we went to dinner. She volunteered to drive and she picked the restaurant. Belucci was a fashionable spot in Miami that served nouveau cuisine in an over-styled South Beach deco setting.

Over dinner, we made the small talk necessary to get to know one another. Jane was raised in Ohio by her single father. He owned a dive bar, and she hung out there and did her homework there after school as kid. She also served drinks and tended bar there before she was legally old enough to do so.

"It was that kind of place," she said by way of explanation. "You

know."

At fifteen, she quit school, packed a backpack and rode to Florida on the back of her eighteen-year-old boyfriend's Harley. As she put it to me at the time, the romance didn't last, and at seventeen she was on her own in Fort Lauderdale, where she had been ever since. She said the climate agreed with her, and I figured she wasn't just talking about the weather.

When she asked what I did, I told her it was none of her business.

"Touché," she said and raised her glass of white wine.

"I'm in the computer business," I said.

"Uh huh," she said in a way that let me know she didn't buy it.

"This is what I do," she said, "My boyfriend goes around and buys scrap gold and we re-sell it."

She said "boyfriend" as casually as if she were mentioning a sick aunt back home. I tried not to flinch.

"And you make enough doing that to afford that condo and that Benz?" I said eyeing the diamonds in her ears and the gold tennis bracelet on her wrist.

"The price goes up all the time," she said, "In the last year it's doubled. It's almost 900 dollars an ounce now."

That story sounded pretty good, but it still sounded like a story.

She might just as well have said she was in the computer business.

After dinner, we had drinks in a noisy, neon-lit club. We did lines and made out in the bathroom. At one in the morning, she drove us back to the Seagate Villa in Fort Lauderdale.

We went out three or four more times and each time she would mention her boyfriend in an offhand way. I was curious about him, but I never asked any questions because I didn't want to ruin a good thing.
She also kept saying that she was "looking for a guy with the right weight," as if I ought to know what that meant. But I didn't. It was another mystery about Jane that I expected would unravel when the time was right. Until then, I was content to keep things loose and indefinite.

Every night that we went out, when we got back to the Seagate Villa, I would ask her up to my place, and she always refused for one reason or another. Then, finally, one night she said yes.

When we got inside, I put on the Phil Collins tape and told her to make herself comfortable. She sat on my black leather sofa, and I got a bottle of tequila out of the freezer and poured some for us.

"Your place is laid out a little different than ours," she said. The use of the plural was a subtle reminder that somewhere she had a boyfriend.

Again, I didn't take the bait.

"Oh yeah?" I said and emptied a little pile of coke out onto a mirror that I kept for just that purpose. With a razor, I chopped out four lines and snorted two of them with a short silver straw while Jane enumerated the ways that my condo was different than hers. I passed the rig over to her and topped off our glasses.

She did her two lines and pinched her nose. I cut out four more as big as the others. We did those and I turned up the music and poured more tequila.

"You really like this song, huh?" she said.

"Yeah, I love it."

By the time the tape clicked over to the other one and back again, we were loaded, and that's what did it. Jane sat up and started talking, loud and fast.

The boyfriend who brought her to Fort Lauderdale on the back of his motorcycle had connections to a biker gang and some drug smugglers. She didn't use drugs then and was more responsible than her boyfriend, who was addicted to pain-killers. She was also a minor and he used her as a mule. In time, the smugglers only wanted to deal with Jane who was always lucid and reliable, unlike her junkie boyfriend.

One night, he sent her to sell a kilo of baking soda to the biker gang for $40,000 dollars. He took the money and split without telling her. The next afternoon, the bikers kidnapped Jane and held her for ransom. Her boyfriend came back to Fort Lauderdale only because he was jonesing and found out about the kidnapping. An attack of conscience sent him to the smugglers to borrow the ransom, which was the original $40,000 dollars plus damages $20,000.

The ransom was paid and Jane, who had been repeatedly raped and beaten, was dumped in the street in front of her boy-friend's house. She had two black eyes, a dislocated shoulder, and a case of gonorrhea. Strangely, it wasn't enough to make her breakup with her boyfriend, but their roles in the drug dealing business flipped, and she became the brains and he the bagman. Working with the smugglers who had fronted her ransom money, she ramped up the business and had some of her old dropout friends from the midwest come down and transport loads of drugs, which widened her distribution of weed and coke.

A month after Jane turned seventeen, the police found her boyfriend dead in the trunk of a car, stripped nude with his hands cut off. That was ten years ago.

"What happened to his hands?" I asked.

"I don't know. They never found 'em," she giggled. "Got anymore of that coke?"

After a story like that, I felt like the least I could do was open up about my own biography. My boyhood of weed dealing and trips to Panama seemed quaint by comparison, and when I got to my current coke dealing, at a pace of two kilos a month, she laughed.

"What's that? Five, ten grand a month?" she said. "The dollars are flying right over your head."

I was at a rare loss for anything to say.

"Man, I'm looking for the right weight," she said, "I gotta find the right weight."

"What does that mean? You keep saying that?"

"My boyfriend used to be a thousand pound man. That's the right weight."

"Your boyfriend used to weigh a thousand pounds?" I said. I couldn't picture it.

She laughed again and touched my face with smooth, cool fingers. "No. No, he bought a thousand pounds of pot at a time."

"Well, damn," I said not trying to hide that I was impressed.

"Yep. The right weight," she nodded, "The reason I'm into buying and selling gold now is all our smuggling friends retired or got busted." A shadow crossed her face, and her voice fell slightly, but noticeably. "Yeah, we lost all our connections, but I had saved some money, so now I'm in the gold business. But man, I'd love to get a good connection again."

"One with the right weight," I said before she could.

She nodded.

I told her I would work on it.

She smiled and there was sympathy in her eyes. I wasn't sure whom it was for.

A few days later, I went to Jorge and told him that I wanted to get a wholesale pot connection, like right off the boat.

"This is your lucky day, Gringo." Jorge said, picking up the name always used by TK and TJ. "This weed is going to cost you. No more Panama Red at $10 a pound. This is seedless sensimilla and cleaned of stems. Just bud, man, just bud."

"But I am looking for weight!" Usually Sensi comes in smaller quantities.

"A dude just paid me a big cocaine debt with 6 tons of bud, 12,000 pounds that I have stashed in a safe house."

"Before you give me a price, I want to lay out the deal." Latinos hate surprises, childhood friend or not, Latinos hate surprises. "Jorge, I met a girl named Jane who seems to be on the level. Her friend in Ohio can do 1,000 pounds of marijuana every

4-5 weeks and has the cash to pay for each 1,000 pound load. So, what I want is the whole 12,000 pounds and a price based on my taking and paying for 1,000 pounds every month for one year."

"You want the whole load, but I have to warehouse it and pay for security?"

"Yes."

"That's gonna cost you, Gringo. I've got $400 in it, wanted to make $200 more, but the warehouse and security is going to cost you

$100 more. That brings the total to $700 per pound."

"$700 per pound! *Chinga!*"

"*No chiste.*"

"Let me see this seedless weed. I'll need a half pound for samples." The marijuana was as advertised. Individual pounds could be sold for $2,000, and 100 pound lots could sell for $1,200 a pound. So, I put $200 a pound on it for me, and priced it to Jane and Danny for $900.

When I told Jane the deal, she lit up and said, "This is what I wanna do: I'm not gonna hang you guys up because I don't wanna be involved. He'll come down and pay for half the load. You take the load up, and he'll pay the other half within two or three days. You come back, pay me, and all I want is twenty dollars a pound. You take a thousand, that's 20,000. Plus as a bonus, if he does 10,000 pounds this year, I want you to buy me a new Rolex and a new Mercedes."

As Jane laid out the plan, I was held transfixed by her unblinking eye contact. Hers were the bluest eyes that I had ever seen and electricity danced within them, charged by her excitement over the "right weight" and the high dollar amounts. I completely lost track of what she was saying midway through it.

I didn't know to whom "he" referred or what she meant by "take the load up," but I figured there would be plenty of time to get all that straight. All I knew for sure was that she wanted an affirmative response, and that I wanted to give her what she wanted, whatever that happened to be.

After a beat, I blinked heavily and said, "okay."

Jane was basically out of the loop from there. She had me come to her condo for drinks and to meet her boyfriend. I was expecting a man in his thirties, or maybe an older burned out sugar-daddy type.
Danny, however, was the last thing I expected.

He looked to be just out of high school with shaggy, blonde, sun-bleached hair, tanned skin, and a very athletic build. It was hard to believe that this was the kid who used to buy a thousand pounds of weed at a time. It's a strange business.

The night we met happened to be his twenty-first birthday. We did some coke and drank a toast to our new partnership. Then, we got into Jane's 450SL and went to Miami to celebrate.

The celebration ended up lasting four straight days. Running on cocaine and tequila, we went from the Seagate Villa to Miami nightclubs and to the beach. Because we didn't sleep, I had plenty of time to get know Danny.

He and Jane were from the same town in Ohio, and he had fallen in love with her when he was just a kid. She was a few years older than him, and his love went unrequited, but he never stopped carrying the torch, even when she dropped out of school and rode away to Florida.

The youngest son of a well-heeled Ohio family, Danny never had to take school very seriously, and, instead of learning anything, he poured himself into a variety of expensive, time-consuming hobbies including dirt bike racing and pot smoking. By the time he was sixteen, he was great at both those things. Being on the teenage dirt bike circuit, he got to know lots of drug dealers in the tri-state area. But all he really cared about was Jane. He started going down to Florida to hang out with her and her junkie boyfriend and he got to know their drug connections. At seventeen, he was running thousand pound loads of drugs from Florida to Ohio.

When Jane's boyfriend was murdered, and had his hands cut off, there was Danny, already on the scene flush with motocross winnings and drug money, and poised to take possession of a considerable trust fund. Jane loved his money and intermittently appreciated his adoration, but it was obvious that she basically regarded him as a pet that could feed itself.

In a way, I felt sorry for Danny, but he was technically an adult, and if he wanted to play lap dog to a faithless, but no less bewitching gold digger, well, that was his business. Indeed, Jane was the most alluring woman I had ever met, and even I, with my keen instinct for self-preservation, found myself disconcertingly eager to make her happy.

One night in a club, I had offhandedly remarked to Jane that money couldn't buy happiness. I don't remember what we were talking about, but I remember the look she gave me when she said, "Honey, you just don't know where to shop."

After four frenzied days of drinking and drugging, I got the call from Jorge. Danny and I, exhausted and totally strung out, loaded 1,000 pounds of pot, half of which Danny paid for as planned, into a U-Haul truck. We covered it with tarps and an innocuous assortment of building materials and padlocked it.

I slept for four hours that night, more than I had in the past five days. It wasn't nearly enough. In the morning, I was behind the wheel of the U-Haul driving Danny and me to Ohio to sell the dope. That's what I thought I was doing anyway.

"There's been a change of plans," Danny said once we pulled onto the interstate. That's a disheartening thing to hear at the outset of any mission, especially an illegal one. "You gotta take me to the airport."

"The airport?" I said. "What for?"

"I gotta get up there ahead of you and get the money all lined

up."

"You're kidding me."

"I wish I was, dude, but that's how it's gotta be," he said avoiding looking at me. "Get off right here," he said pointing to the airport exit. "I can't miss my plane."

I didn't like it, but there was nothing I could do. I pulled off the interstate.

The Fort Lauderdale-Hollywood International Airport was small and tidy. I stopped at the edge of the long-term parking lot, a hundred yards from the terminal. From there, I could easily get back on the interstate.

"Here you go," I said testily.

"Come on, man, pull up there," said Danny sniffing and pointing to the terminal. "I think my nose is bleeding. Is my nose bleeding?"

"No," I said without looking at him and drove toward the terminal against my better judgment. Had I been more alert and thinking more clearly, I might have noticed the sign indicating the low clearance of the overhang above the terminal entrance.

From above came a sharp bang and the dull, sickening sound of metal grinding against metal. The truck then jerked to a stop and I knew immediately what had happened. We were stuck.

Danny and I looked at each other wide-eyed with our mouths hanging open. A surge of adrenaline coursed through my body and chased away the lingering hangover of the past few days. All at once, I was stone cold sober and very much awake. All around us, arriving and departing travelers and tourists were staring at the truck. I threw it in reverse and stomped the gas. No good.

Danny, suddenly, grabbed his bag off the floorboard, jumped out of the truck and disappeared through the automatic doors of the terminal. He never said anything and he didn't look back.

An immense security guard in a khaki colored uniform and hat appeared beside the truck waving his arms for me to back up. He was saying something I couldn't make out.

"It's stuck!" I shouted.

He climbed up on the bumper and started bouncing up and down. He must have been 350 pounds.

"Back up! Back it up!" He was yelling and sweating and bouncing for all he was worth, but the truck wouldn't budge.

A crowd was starting to form, and I knew it wouldn't be long before the police arrived. Something had to be done and fast.

I opened my door without a plan, but by the time my feet hit the pavement I had it. I knelt down, and with trembling hands, I frantically unscrewed the little caps and pressed the valves releasing the air from the tires. It came out with a life-saving hiss. After I had done this to all the tires, I got back in the truck, started it up and tried to reverse. I was still stuck. The fat security guard resumed his bouncing and again I mashed the gas.

"Move you bastard!" I screamed as rising waves of panic turned my blood to ice.

Suddenly, there was a metallic pop and the security guard fell off the front of the truck as it bolted backwards. I was free.

I backed away from the terminal as quickly as the flat tires would let me and lurched away from the airport. I was sweating and panting and continuously checking the side view mirror as I slowly and unsteadily made my way to a filling station a quarter mile away.

I stopped beside the air hoses, cut the engine, and smoked a cigarette with shaking hands. After a second cigarette, my pulsed had almost returned to normal and my hands were steady. I took a deep breath, got out, and aired up the tires.

The rising sun had just broken over the tops of the palm trees. There was no wind and it was already hot. The humidity made it seem like I was breathing soup.

Two lonely days later, I was in Ohio. I met up with Danny who conspicuously never asked how I got the truck unstuck. I was just as happy not to revisit the incident. Thirty-six hours later, he had all the money together just like he promised. He paid me, we unloaded the weed, and I drove back to Florida.

Jane was certainly pleased with how everything had gone. That, combined with having the whole nerve-rattling affair over with, made me happy, but again I thought that there had to be a better way to get ahead in the drug business.

One evening, after I had been back from Ohio for a couple of days and was almost caught up on my sleep, I was alone in my condo smoking a joint, drinking tequila and listening to the Eagles Greatest Hits on cassette. When "Peaceful Easy Feeling" came on, I poured another drink, walked out onto the balcony, and looked at the soft purple sky. It was streaked with jagged pink and red clouds. Across the way, Jane's balcony was empty and her light was out. That was okay with me. The stone balcony was warm under my bare feet, and I felt almost like myself again.

11 - TAKE IT TO THE LIMIT

A few days later, I decided to do myself the favor of getting out of Miami for a few days and I went to see Ronnie. It had been a few years since I had last seen him, but I knew that he was living out in the sticks of northern Alabama.

I looked him up and found him in an old house trailer that sat in the middle of twenty acres of dry grassland. He had gotten his commercial driver's license and bought his own cab and car hauler. They were parked next to his trailer with tall weeds grown up around the tires.

In his kitchen, we caught up over beers and a joint. It turned out that things weren't going so well for Ronnie. His hair was cut short, which somewhat tamed its natural wildness, and his face sagged. He told me that hauling cars, when he was lucky enough to get the work, was tough.

"How did you get the truck in the first place?" I asked.

"I borrowed the down payment from my dad," he said and picked at the label of his Coors. "I'm three months behind on it, and it's not looking good for next month."

Money wasn't a problem for me. I happened to be flush with cash, and I was also looking for a change. As we sat and talked, the answer became obvious.

"How would you like to work for me exclusively?" I said. "You could drive out of Miami running pot up to Ohio. Just drop it off, stay three or four days and drive back with the money. After that, you'll be off for about twenty days and then you can just do the same thing again."

He didn't say anything, but I could tell he was thinking it over.

I said, "You know what we used to say when we were kids: 'let us be friends as long we want and never want as long as we're friends.'"

He just smiled, nodded, and shook my hand. His eyes were bright and he looked more like the guy I used to know.

"I'll be right back," I said and jumped up.

From the trunk of my car, I pulled a canvas duffle bag and brought it in the trailer. I put the bag on the table and pulled 20,000 dollars in cash out of it. Ronnie looked at the money and back at me.

"That's 10,000 dollars to repay your dad, 3,000 for you to catch up on your payments on the truck, 2,000 for the fuel, and 5,000 to get your shit back in order," I said. "Be in Miami in three weeks."

And three weeks later, Ronnie showed up in Miami with five cars on the hauler. He had taken the five grand and bought five old cars and strapped them down. When he got to Miami, we put 200 pounds of weed in the trunk of each car. That was his idea, and I thought it was pretty ingenious. Then, he went north.

A week after that, he was back with the money. I paid him twenty dollars on every pound, the same rate that Jane got. He made 20,000 dollars a load and was really happy with that. I was really happy with it too because I didn't have to make the trip. I was freed up to get in a lot more trouble in Miami.

12 - SUMMERTIME

There was never a more comfortable place and time for newly rich, sensation-crazed, cokeheads and swingers than Fort Lauderdale in the summer of 1984. It was as magical and loud as a fireworks display.

Dennis was still coming by once a month and picking up a couple of keys and running his route. Ronnie was taking a thousand pounds of weed a month in the car hauler. Their schedules were staggered so that they were never in Miami at the same time. The money and drugs just flowed.

Jane didn't go to any of the warehouses to do deals herself; she never actually saw a load come or go. She just collected her cut as an investor and that was it. She was doing lots of coke and starting to become a bit isolated and unpredictable. Two or three times a week, I would see her and have drinks, but we mainly just cracked each other up in a friendly way or else talked business.

I made every effort to date her, which almost always involved spending lots of money. I could tell she would be a high-maintenance girlfriend, but I still found her exhilarating to be around. I wanted to be with her more than I ever wanted to be with anyone. We spoke the same language.

Luckily, it seemed that for Danny the fire had at last gone out. He had gone back to Ohio and didn't come down to Miami anymore. As far as I knew, he and Jane no longer spoke. I kept in touch with him through Ronnie who was delivering pot to him. Danny was riding dirt bikes, but just for fun, not competitively, dealing weed on his own, and working in the family real-estate business, not that he really needed to.

Every afternoon at five o'clock, Jane had a stiff and spicy Bloody Mary. In her disorganized life, it was a reassuring ritual. With religious consistency, no matter where she happened to be, at home, on a boat at the marina, or on an airplane, she had a Bloody Mary garnished with a stalk of celery. At bars and restaurants, I saw her send back more than a few that came to her garnished with green olives, pickled peppers, or pearl onions. Only celery would do.

Whenever Ronnie got back to Miami with the money from one of his runs up to Ohio, and after he took his cut, Jane insisted on seeing the rest of the cash. She had a money counting machine that she claimed she had bought for her gold business. She loved to count money.

About once a month, I would come by her condo with a duffle bag full of cash and drop it on her living room floor. Instantly, she would light up like a kid at Christmas, and she would pull out her Cummins Allison money counting machine. Just as she was particular about having celery in her Bloody Marys, she had to have her twenty grand in crisp, clean, new hundred dollar bills. She called it her Clean Twenty.
Then, she would run the bills through her machine, bundle them up into thousands, and band them with Number 16 Sparco rubber bands which she always had on hand. She enjoyed the routine and worked on it with unbroken concentration.

It would take me probably eight hours to count that much money, but Jane would knock it out in two. In the end, all her cash would be neatly stacked and wrapped.

Jorge was always impressed, and he greatly appreciated the care with which Jane approached the counting and stacking of the bills. When I would take him his cut of the money, he would laugh and say, "That girl, Jane, she does a good job. I don't even have to count it; I just weigh it."

One afternoon, after the money was all counted and stacked, and Jorge's cut was separated from hers and mine, she was more ebullient than usual.

"Perfect timing!" she said looking at her Rolex. It was exactly five o'clock. "Let's have a Bloody Mary." She was already getting the glasses out of a kitchen cabinet and a handle of Absolut out of the freezer.

We toasted with our drinks that were more pink than blood red because there was so much vodka in them. She winked at me as she took a bite of her celery. Loosened up and talkative, she asked if I had any blow on me. I didn't. I was positive that she had some, but she was never one to do her own drugs if she could do somebody else's. She stuck out her lower lip in an exaggerated, juvenile pout.

I had two thick joints in my shirt pocket so we smoked one of those and listened to Culture Club's "Colour by Numbers" on cassette tape, her choice.

"I gotta go take Jorge his money," I said, picking up the neat stacks of bills from the coffee table and returning them to the duffle bag. "I'll be back about eight, then we'll go somewhere and celebrate."

"Someplace nice," she said. "Not some cheap ass place on the beach. okay, Stein?"

That was a little nickname she had for me, Steven Stein.

"Very funny," I said. "Be ready at eight. Why don't you try wearing something besides a bathing suit? We won't be going to some cheap ass place on the beach. I'm wearing a tux and I don't want you embarrassing me."

"Get out of here," she said laughing.

At eight sharp I was at her door wearing my tuxedo, the one I bought in high school. It still fit perfectly. I could tell Jane was impressed. She looked gorgeous in a short, but not too short, black dress.

I told her she looked great.

"I'm wearing a bathing suit underneath," she said.

"We'll see about that," I said. "Come on, let's go."

She insisted on driving, which was nothing new, and we went to The Palms in Miami. We had cocktails before dinner and we danced afterward. Jane was drinking gin and tonics the whole time and drinking them quickly, as if she were on a mission. If we had been doing coke, it wouldn't have mattered as much, but we weren't, and she got very drunk.

I drove us back to the Seagate Villa and walked her up to her condo. She was laughing and slurring her way through some long, stupid story that I didn't understand. When we got inside, she kicked off her high heels and put on a Rod Stewart tape. Then, she flopped down on her pale, pink, leather couch and I sat down next to her. After a still moment, she turned and looked at me with unfocused eyes. Suddenly, she leaned in and kissed me on the mouth.

We started making out and I thought, "Finally. This is it."

She didn't seem blacked out or anything, so I didn't have any reservations about going as far as she would let me.

"Stay here tonight," she whispered.

"I will," I said.

Just then, "Some Guys Have All the Luck" came on and Jane pushed back from me and said, "Let's have some champagne," she got up and went in the kitchen.

That's not what I was in the mood for, but she seemed determined. She pulled a bottle of Dom Perignon out of the refrigerator and started struggling with the foil and the wire on top.

"Here," I said reaching for the bottle, "Let me."

I should have just let her open it, but I wanted to look good. I gave the cork a twist and started easing it out. Then, I got my thumbs under it and pushed. The cork popped out and hit Jane square in the forehead. She dropped to the kitchen tile like she'd been shot with a gun. For a second, I just stood and stared, horrified as champagne gushed all over the floor. Then suddenly, without getting up, she vomited. Needless to say, the magic was gone.

For the next two hours, I sat in the cold, bright light of the bathroom while Jane intermittently threw up in the toilet. When she finally passed out from exhaustion, I picked her up and put her in bed. I pulled her dress off and sure enough, she had a bikini on underneath. I covered her up and went to sleep on the couch. Sometimes in life when a moment passes, it passes for good.

13 - MERCEDES-BENZ

One afternoon a couple weeks after our ill-fated date, or whatever it had been, I knocked on Jane's door.

"How would you like to go out on my boat?" I asked.

Trying to find ways to spend more time with her, I had bought a boat, specifically a Sea Ray Monaco SRV 207, which I kept docked at the marina.

"Awesome," she said. "Come on in. Want a drink? Want a

toot?"

"Yes to both," I said and sat down on her angular, pink couch.

When she bent over to put our drinks on the reflective black acrylic coffee table, I wanted to grab her small waist and press my thumbs into the dimples of Venus on her lower back that were peaking out between her cropped t-shirt and flowered bikini bottoms. Instead, I just watched her sit down and we had a polite drink. We did a couple of lines and made a plan to take the boat out the following day.

Early the next morning, we went to a breakfast buffet and ate. We were the youngest people in the place at that hour by a margin of twenty-five years. And I felt like a teenager on a date, trying to shake the sense that this girl was out of my league. Jane made everything feel new.

The clear, dry morning pointed toward a beautiful day. Cool air whipped through the car as we drove down to the marina. On the way, we put up the windows to get a joint lit. We had just finished smoking it and tossed the roach out when we heard the piercing squeal of a siren behind us.

"Dammit!"

I pulled to the right and did my best to seem totally sober and casual. In the glove compartment was a half-ounce of weed, and I was sure the car still smelled like smoke. You could practically smell it. The policeman stepped out of his car and walked slowly up to my window.

After he looked at my driver's license, copied the information, and handed it back he said, "I stopped you because you got a tail light that's out. And now that I'm up here, I can smell marijuana in the vehicle."

"Oh that's-" My mind was racing, my voice sounded as if it was coming from somewhere outside. He cut me off before I could finish formulating an explanation.

"Don't make this difficult," he said and waved toward himself. "Get out. Get out of the car."

"I'm not gonna make trouble," I said.

"Come on. Let's go."

Moving to unfasten my seat belt, I noticed a distinct, burnt hole in his uniform shirt. Almost all of my t-shirts had holes exactly the same size in about the same place. They appeared when smoldering pot seeds would pop out of a bowl, land on my chest, and burn a hole in my shirt. His was right below his name-tag that read BAKER.

"I do have some weed in the car. There's a half-ounce of it in a tin in the glovebox. I'll hand it to you. It's really excellent stuff."

He didn't change his hard expression, but he had quit gesturing for me to get out.

I got the tin out of the glove compartment and handed it over. As he took it from me, just to see how he would react, I said, "There you go. It's yours. I'm handing it over." Then, as instructed I got out of the car and repeated, "It's excellent, really."

He opened the tin, took a long look and smiled behind his black shades.

"There are papers in there too," I said, "Zig Zag's."

Carrying the tin, Baker walked over to Jane's side of the car, and his face was again set in a stone mask.

"Anything in your purse I need to know about?" he said.

There was no response from Jane. She just kept staring straight ahead looking mad.

"Let me take a look at the purse," said Baker.

Jane, reluctantly, handed her purse out the window, but before Baker even got it open, Jane started crying and wailing so suddenly and vehemently that it made Baker and me both jump.

He put the bag on the hood of the car, looked in and pulled out an eight ball of coke. I had no idea Jane had it. She hadn't mentioned it to me. I just stood there not knowing what to say or do, or if anything would even help. I looked at Baker, shaking my head hoping to communicate my ignorance of the coke.

I thought, "He's going to arrest us, or keep the drugs, or both."

Jane was still screaming in what was approaching a full-on hysterical fit.

Baker looked at me, his face full of gray malevolence. He held out the bag of coke and said, "You know about this?"

I put my hands up. "No. I didn't. I swear."

My heart was racing and no other words would form in my mouth. He looked at me and smiled, bigger than he had before, showing a perfect row of top teeth.

"Okay, I believe you," he said and walked around the front of the car toward me. "You looked so shocked." He gave a short laugh and said, "Yeah, I could tell you got caught flat-footed."

He stuffed the eight ball in the tin with the pot, closed the lid, and held it to his side with one hand.

Again, Baker turned to cold granite. "I know your names and I know where you live." He paused to let it sink in. "I don't want to hear anything about this. Ever."

"No problem," I said. "Thank you, Officer Baker. We certainly do appreciate that."

Without another word, he got in his car and drove off ahead of us.

Jane had quit hollering, but she was still freaked out and breathing hard.

I pulled a hard u-turn and headed back to Seagate Villa. We got more coke, and more pot, and headed back to the marina. By the time we got there, we weren't talking about the setback with Officer Baker or Jane's over the top freak out anymore. We got on the Sea Ray and had a great day on the water.

In Ohio, Danny was moving a thousand pounds every month to five weeks, all of it coming from me. By the end of the year, he had taken in 10,000 pounds. I went up there with Ronnie and the last load to celebrate the achievement.

Over tequila and cocaine, I was laughing and said, "I guess Jane is gonna get her bonus."

He got really serious and said, "What do you mean?"

"I'm paying her twenty bucks a pound and if she does 10,000 pounds, as a bonus, I have to buy her a new Rolex and a new 450."

"You're kidding," said Danny.

"I know," I laughed. "The one she's got is only a year or two old."

Danny didn't see the humor in it. He told me he had the same arrangement with Jane. We realized that between us we were giving her 400 grand, two Rolex watches, a ten-karat diamond tennis bracelet, a Mercedes-Benz 450SL and a Corvette. She always called me Stein because she thought I was cheap. I called her the Black Widow, and only one of us was joking.

With less subtlety than ever before, Jane was single-mindedly driven by material comfort and security. Everything she did was in service to those ideals. Her speech was peppered with dollar amounts, brand names, and the names at the top of Forbes' list of the world's billionaires.

Every time I went to her condo, she had the Miami Herald open to the Social section. She knew what parties to attend and who was buying, what was selling and for how much.

At her Christmas party in her condo, I had a few drinks and told her she was getting to be a bore.

"Listen, in five minutes you can marry more money than you can earn in a lifetime," she said defensively.

"You have half-a-million dollars, and three cars as it is. You have more jewelry, clothes, and coke than you know what do with. What do you need with so much stuff?"

She didn't say anything, but I could tell we were going

past the failsafe. This was going to be the last night of our business together. The lights went out in her eyes. Under all the jewelry and makeup she wore, she looked older than her twenty-eight years. She seemed to be desperately clinging to youth, instead of enjoying it. She looked at me as if I were an empty shirt flapping on a clothesline and said, as though it were obvious, "All this stuff, it's bait. For the big fish."

At a gala charity event on New Year's Eve, she met William Rossler, the first real estate billionaire in Miami. By January fifth, she quit returning my calls.

In May, I saw in the newspaper that Jane had landed her big fish; she married the fifty-three-year-old Rossler. Movers came to clear out Jane's condo at the Seagate Villa and that was it.

One day at happy hour, I bumped into a local weed dealer I used to see at parties. He knew Jane and had been at her last Christmas party. We started talking about Jane. The whole time I knew her, she always wore a big tacky necklace with a thick, tear-drop locket. It looked like the kind you could pick up for ten bucks on the boardwalk. The weed dealer told me he heard that Rossler wanted her to get rid of it and wear something more elegant. She opened it and showed him that inside was a cashier's check for 250,000 dollars. She was the first and last woman I ever knew who had a bigger game going, than I did.

14 - PEOPLE GET READY

In my experience with it, the marijuana trade was relatively laid back and it engendered complicity that felt something like trust amongst the players. Even with hundreds of thousands of dollars on the line, everybody involved was more mellow and possessed of more accommodating attitudes. By contrast, the coke business was intense and nervous. There was a palpable and ever-present threat of violence. So far, I had been able to operate at a somewhat safe level of remove. Jorge, who navigated the filth and breathed the chaos like it was oxygen, insulated me from the more deadly aspects of the business. Even so, except for my guys and him, the business was full of people who were categorically strung out, paranoid, deceitful, and just plain weird.

Weed is what I really loved. But this time, I wanted to be the source. I wanted to grow it myself, and after some careful research, I decided Jamaica would be the perfect place to grow on the scale that I envisioned. I decided to go see Ronnie.

I hadn't seen him since early December when he took the last load of weed to the midwest and brought the money back. In late January of 1985, I went to his place in Alabama. He had managed to hold onto most of the money he made in the last year. That spring, he had been planning on building a log cabin on his property. He described the layout and showed me where he planned to build it.

As the sun went down, we smoked joints and drank beer in the kitchen of his trailer. I asked about Danny and how he was doing.

"He made some connections out West," Ronnie said, "He says he can get weed from Arizona for 500 a pound. The only snag is getting it from Arizona to Ohio. He doesn't know how he's going to do that."

Even so, it was a move Danny had to make. We had been delivering to him for 900 a pound. Once he figured out the transportation, he obviously stood to make a lot more money getting pot elsewhere.

"There's no way I'm doing it," said Ronnie and took a toke. "Man, there's nothing but a bunch of crackheads on the route now," he added, "It's probably even worse out west; I don't know."

"You know, we should just go back to only selling weed." It was the first time that I had said it out loud, and it sounded right.

Ronnie sat forward with his forearms on the table. "I thought about that," he said. "When I get my cabin built, I'm gonna try to grow some."

I said, "I've been thinking about growing some too. A lot of it." I proceeded to tell him my plan. He was in.

Other than his log cabin idea, there was nothing much keeping Ronnie in northern Alabama. He wasn't attached to anyone or anything. I didn't want to see him drift back toward the twilight of underemployed boredom and criminality that have claimed better men.

Ronnie started gathering marijuana seeds and planting them in the woods around his property, and in five-gallon buckets inside his trailer. It took about four months for the plants to mature and go to seed. We were only interested in harvesting the seeds. We were going to need a lot of them.

In the meantime, I flew to Jamaica and checked into a hotel.

For a week, I looked in the paper for houses, condos, and other places to rent that had gates around them or some other measure of security. I was still making steady money in Miami every month handing cheap kilos of coke over to Dennis, so I could afford to rent at the top of the market, and I only considered the nicest places.

I finally settled on an estate and I signed a six-month lease to start. The deal came with a maid named Kit and a grounds-keeper, her brother Winston.

Once enough seeds were harvested in north Alabama, Ronnie and I brought them over to Jamaica. We stashed all the seeds in pill bottles and any other type of handy, relatively inconspicuous container. Nothing flying into Jamaica was checked very carefully. It was only what came out of Jamaica that got checked. Cops and customs agents didn't care what went into Jamaica.

We planted the seeds in the gardens and in various places around the estate, and let the plants go to seed again. Then, we started trying to find land where we could start growing on a large scale.

While we looked, Ronnie and I enjoyed Jamaica immensely. We drank rum all day, smoked huge amounts of cheap weed, and hung out at the beach. I bought food for everyone at the estate, and at night Kit would cook for us.

She was in her early twenties with dark brown almond-shaped eyes, light skin, aquiline features and a compact, athletic build. Loose natural ringlets of black hair fell past her shoulders. Her mother, who was always referred to as Mrs. Williams, even by Kit, was herself the product of a black Jamaican father and a white English mother. Kit's own father was a strict, white, English fundamentalist. Her half-brother, Winston, had a Jamaican father. The difference of paternity was obvious. Winston was four years older than Kit. He was, as the saying goes, tall, dark, and handsome. Their outward differences belied a deep bond between them.

Kit and I also developed a bond. I would hang around while she cleaned or arranged the flowers that Winston had clipped from the garden. Her poise and simple, direct point-of-view fascinated me. I asked her about her upbringing in the rural Jamaican hills. She was no less thoughtful for the quickness and brevity of her answering. Any topic that arose in conversation seemed to be one that she had already carefully considered.

Some nights, I would go to Montego Bay get drunk, and come home early in the morning. One such morning, Kit was awake and we had sex.

She had a four-year-old daughter by a dark-skinned Jamaican man who disappeared as soon as it was clear Kit was pregnant. Mrs.
Williams took the baby because she said Kit was too young to care for it properly. That may have been true, but it was also obvious to Kit that her parents were deeply ashamed because she had an illegitimate child. Except for Winston, Kit was estranged from her family, and her daughter was kept away from her. They hadn't seen each other in more than two years.

Winston was very protective of Kit, and, once it was clear that she and I were sleeping together, he became surly and stubborn.
Eventually, we settled our differences and everyone in the house got along well. Ronnie was as energetic and easy-going as I ever knew him to be. Under the Jamaican influence, he relaxed his already casual bathing and grooming habits. He just swam in the pool now and then and left it at that. His wild mane of hair was a perennial point of curiosity for the locals who had never seen such hair on a white person.

My new living arrangement, and having relationships that were based on something other than cocaine and money, were helping me dry out. I wasn't doing coke in Jamaica, but I hadn't kicked it completely.

Once a month, I flew to Miami for a few days to get paid and give Dennis the re-up. When I was there, I would stay high the whole time. Cocaine is a hell of a drug; once you get hooked it takes a good long while to get off it completely.

I was only selling two kilos a month, but I was making 20,000 dollars on each one. I made 40,000 dollars a month for what amounted to an hour's worth of work, not counting travel time. When I landed in Miami, I would check into a hotel, always the same one, and get with Jorge. For a couple of days, I would do coke and sit around the pool, waiting. Jorge would send over a connection with my two kilos, and I would pay him. A day or two after that, Dennis would come down, pay me for the previous load, and I would give him the two new kilos. He didn't have to call; he knew where to find me.

Dealing with Dennis, there was never any anxiety. He was totally reliable. I would load him up and he would take off again in his van. I put some of the money in a safe deposit box and took the rest back to Jamaica. It was a no-hassle routine that kept everybody happy, busy, and with fatter bank accounts than they ever had before. That was the routine for the next three years.

I was in love with Kit and I wanted to commit to her more than leaving once a month to be a totally different person would allow. I felt that Jamaica was changing me for the better, and I was ready to let it happen.

15 - WHITE LINES

In the summer of 1986, All-American college basketball star Len Bias died of a cocaine overdose; It happened just two days after being drafted by the Boston Celtics. A former athlete myself, the news shook me. The cocaine business was getting everybody killed.

The network of dealers on Dennis' route that I depended on to move the coke had rapidly degenerated into a desperate bunch of common addicts and thieves at best and paranoid, violent crazies at worst. Having been down the bleak road of cocaine addiction myself, I maintained a wary sympathy for them as long as I could, which wasn't very long. Unlike me, none of those guys were doing anything to dig themselves out of their worsening situations. Almost without exception, all my guys, who had once been relatively reliable, had gone from snorting coke, to freebasing and, then, to cooking and smoking crack.

If Dennis or I dropped off a pound of coke, I had absolutely no assurance that these dealers weren't going to smoke an ounce of it themselves, and if/when they did, 2,000 dollars would just go right up in smoke. In fact, that's about the only thing I could count on them to do. To make up the loss, they resorted to any type of blunt low-life scam their scrambled brains could focus on long enough to carry out. Usually, it was strong-arm robbery, breaking into cars and houses, stealing luggage in airports, and pimping.

Jail sentences (these guys were alarmingly easy for the police to catch), crack psychosis, overdoses, AIDS, and murder had reduced the coke business from high-speed thrills and easy money to a depressing wallow among criminal cast-offs and a jungle tour of urban social ills. I had no taste for it.

I was getting anxious to quit the cocaine business completely and focus on Kit and start a pot farm. However, my income from the coke trade, almost half a million dollars a year, was easy and essential. It would be used to buy the land, pay the crew, and pay for the protections we were going to need to grow weed like I wanted to grow it. Also, to maximize profit and ensure safe delivery, we were also going to need our own boat. I wanted to control everything.

Finding the land was taking longer than I had anticipated. Ronnie and I consulted with Winston to see if he had any ideas. He didn't, but he joined the search and the three of us looked everywhere, high and low.

16 - HOMEGROWN

The marijuana in Jamaica was excellent. It was basically the same stuff that I used to import from Panama, which was sativa, a type of marijuana that gives an energetic, psychedelic high. The plants are tall with long, thin, leaves and the flowers are red and orange. In Jamaica, the sativa was more potent because I was right there at the source and could get it before it had been dried out, mashed flat and cut into bricks with a box cutter.

On one of my stateside trips, I read an article in *High Times* about a type of marijuana growing in Afghanistan, which was called indica. It was described in the article as producing more narcotic effects. Indicas are shorter plants with broad, blue-green colored leaves. The buds can be purple and bright green.

I found Afghanistan on a globe and noticed that it lay on almost the same latitude as north Georgia. When I got back to Jamaica, I told Ronnie what I was thinking. If we could get some indica seeds and start growing those, we would have the purple weed market all to ourselves.

"What about all the seeds and plants we've already got?" said

Ronnie.

"Yeah, I thought about that. We can harvest the plants, and just hang onto the seeds," I said. "We might as well. It won't cost us anything."

He nodded and looked thoughtful. "Where are we

going to get the seeds?" he said.

"I thought about that too," I said and told him my idea.

Ronnie didn't need much convincing. He cleaned up and flew to Afghanistan.

Staying in a hotel, he hung around and tried to meet anybody he thought had the right look. After two months, he met Ardeshir, a young guy who spoke some English. He took Ronnie to an old woman who lived in a cramped house in the countryside. Ardeshir spoke to her and she readily sold him a handful of seeds. They looked okay to Ronnie, and, having no other choice but to take the old woman at her word, he bought the indica marijuana seeds. Then, he and Ardeshir smoked some potent hash and went and had tea.

At the time, Ronnie's bushy hair was long enough to bring together into a ponytail. While he was stoned on the local hash, he got the idea to smuggle the seeds back to the United States in his hair, but was unsure just how to go about it. Ardeshir took Ronnie to his sister's house. She had three daughters with hair almost the color of Ronnie's. She cut the girls' hair and wove it into sacks to hold the seeds. These were then woven into Ronnie's wiry, tangled hair. The next day, he flew back to the States.

I picked him up at the airport in Atlanta when he got back.

"Man, my neck is killing me," Ronnie said when we were driving away.

"Why? What's the matter with your neck?" I asked, but I didn't really care. I was so happy to be away from the airport and out of harm's way.

"I was afraid to move my head the whole time," he said. "I was afraid the seeds would fall out."

"Out of your head? What are you talking about?"

"No, man. My hair," he said and went on to explain how he smuggled the seeds in sacks made out of children's hair that were woven into his own hair.

Safely back at Ronnie's place in Alabama, I cut the seeds out of his hair, which I hated doing. Whenever I thought we had them all, more would shake out and bounce on the kitchen table. In all, he had smuggled about 300 seeds in his hair. Strange as it seemed to me, it was an ingenious plan and had obviously worked flawlessly.

We took the seeds to the Valley and planted them far back on the other side of the creek on my family's property where I had rolled and smoked my first joint more than twenty years before. Then, I went back to Jamaica, leaving Ronnie to keep an eye on the plants. I came back a month later to see them for myself. The young plants were squatty with broad, dark green leaves. The females had bright green and purple flowers with white and orange hairs all over them which were trademarks of an indica. We knew we had what we wanted. We let all the plants go to seed which took three more months.

When they were ready, I went back to Georgia and Ronnie and I harvested about 3,000 seeds. Then, Ronnie and I went down to Miami for a week so I could connect with Jorge, collect from Dennis, give him another load of cocaine, and send him on his way. I was still making 40,000 dollars a month from the cocaine trade. It was more than enough to run the house and start the farm in Jamaica. We returned with thousands of indica seeds and tens of thousands of dollars. So far, so good.

Winston and I planted the new seeds where previously the sativa had grown. We had the same intention with the indica seeds: acclimate, harvest, and store them until we found a place to plant them and start the farm. It took two years to do, but we finally had enough acclimated seeds to grow indica marijuana, a first in Jamaica, on a large scale. But we still needed land, a crew, a boat, and a captain.

One day, Winston greeted me with good news: he found some land for us to use. It was an untamed, jungle valley high in the hills and several rugged miles from the nearest village. Bordered by a high ridge on the western edge, the valley below was empty except for mango and banana trees. A creek ran along the eastern edge. This parcel of jungle was deeded to the Rastafarian church and the local sheriff.

The valley met all of our requirements, but before I could lease the land, Winston, Ronnie, and I had to meet with the sheriff and religious leaders in the nearby village. I gave them some Rolex watches and a pile of cash, which secured their permission to grow marijuana on the land and hire a crew of farmers from the village to help do it. Over time, we came to understand that just because we leased the land and paid off the authorities and religious leaders their cooperation was contingent and protection was not guaranteed. But, for the time being, we were happy with the arrangement we made.

I hired five local guys to clear the land, get it ready, and plant the seeds. They all had their own machetes that they used to chop down small trees and strip the limbs. With the logs, they built forts and shelters for themselves. With that done, they started to clear the valley. While they worked, I flew to Miami, moved a couple of kilos of coke, flew back to Jamaica, and turned my attention to finding a boat and a captain.

By the time I made it back to the valley, the fields had been cleared, tilled, and sown. In addition to that, and as a complete surprise to me, the guys I hired had built larger, more elaborate huts and moved their families into them. There were a dozen kids under the age of five running around the place. My valley farm had been turned into a village.

During the day, the children splashed and swam in the creek that ran through the woods to the east. The growers loved their work and took it seriously. They knew how to deal with pests and what pH balance of the soil was optimal. When the plants started getting tall, they cultivated and pruned the sticky acres of purple and green.

In the evenings after work, they sat and argued in a

good-natured way and talked shop while they smoked chalices and giant spliffs. As their wives made dinner over open fires, the children ran and played noisy games with one another.

I was so enthralled with the way of life on the farm that I asked the men to help me build a hut for myself upstream from where they and their families had theirs. I wanted to be in the fields every day, learning and watching my crop of exotic marijuana develop. Reaching up in the tropical sun, the plants were taller and different every day.

Kit was also growing and developing quickly. She was heavily pregnant, but she would come to the farm occasionally and stay a couple of days with me in the hut where I had taken to sleeping most nights in a sleeping bag. My hut was first to get the clean water coming down from the mountain, and Kit and I went downstream to bathe. Even though the estate I rented had a swimming pool, Ronnie and Winston would come down to the farm too to help out, get high, swim in the creek, and cook out.

There was no alcohol on the farm. The growers were Rastafarians and abstained from drinking as part of their faith. They did, however, smoke pot constantly, which was another tenant of their religion. In spite of, or maybe because of, the crew being high all the time, there was a vital, healthy, and abundant spirit on the farm, and we all enjoyed working together.

During the day, we got by on so-so food, which was

anything edible that grew in the gardens the women tended or on the native fruit trees - anything that could be picked off the ground and eaten. I bought a blue 1966 Ford F-150 pickup truck and, once a month, when I got back from my regular Miami run, I would go to Montego Bay in it and get a load of food and whatever we needed in the way of supplies, like new machetes, batteries, Band-Aids, and rope.

Over the past two and a half years, I had saved enough money to buy a boat and we were just a couple of months away from really needing one. The plants would be harvested in matter of weeks, and then there would be a period of trimming, drying, and curing. After that, it would be time to take the yield to Miami and see what I could do with it there.

Ronnie and I hung around the docks in Montego Bay, but trying to find just the right boat and captain was a slow and frustrating search. The boat had to be big and powerful enough to hide hundreds, and maybe thousands, of pounds of weed and move it across the Bermuda Triangle in hard seas and bad winds.

We often quoted the famous line from the movie *Jaws* to one another, "You're going to need a bigger boat." It became the theme of our search and a personal metaphor for my approach to my business. Whether I was coked up in a Miami nightclub or blissfully stoned and sweating on my Jamaican indica plantation, I was always thinking in terms of "bigger boats."

And one bright, windy morning at the marina, we found one. Somebody was selling an old beam trawler for 300,000 dollars and I paid cash for it. Half the equation was solved, but we still needed a sympathetic captain. As with the boat, we needed someone particular, someone with the right attitude regarding free enterprise and the good sense not to discuss it.

17 - RIDE LIKE THE WIND

I met Halsten late one, muggy night in my favorite bar in Montego Bay. The place had a reliable rhythm of being full until about midnight and then thinning out, leaving only a few to sit and drink in the fading buzz of the earlier hours' sexualized and intoxicated abandon.

A few seats away from me at the bar was a big blonde guy with a thick yellow mustache. I introduced myself, and in a Swedish accent as thick as everything else about him and made thicker still by his drunkenness, he told me that his name was Halsten. He added that he was, in his words, a "lost sailor."

His nose and cheeks were slightly sunburned and the rest of him was ruddy from being blasted by the sun and high, salty winds. On his left forearm was a faded tattoo of a topless hula dancer under a palm tree. Without my asking him anything, he spoke of his poor luck with women, his disgraceful discharge from the Swedish Navy, and that his name meant "rock," an unfortunate irony, given his passion for all manner of floating vessel.

"That is unfortunate," I said. "But meet me tomorrow at the marina. I might have job for you anyway." I had a feeling about Halsten.

We shook on it and I left him alone at the bar bemoaning his lot in a strange accent, in a land of strange accents.

The next day, I was surprised when Halsten was at the marina at the appointed time and place. Other than not removing his aviator sunglasses, he didn't seem at all hungover. He was also a bit easier to understand than he had been at the bar.

I showed him my boat and asked if he had any interest in taking it to Miami and back. He said he liked the boat and that he had lots of experience with yachts and commercial boats of its size. He might be interested in the job, he said, if the price was right, and the price depended on the cargo. Again without my asking, guided by the sonar of the desperado, he ventured that he knew the best covert routes and passages through the tricky Caribbean seas. I guess he had a feeling about me too.

That evening, I brought him up to the estate in the truck to meet Ronnie and Winston. Even though our baby was almost due, Kit insisted on making dinner for everyone. After we ate, Winston rolled some giant spliffs, and we got high by the pool and told Halsten the plan, which served as a job offer. He accepted. We toasted, and late that night, I drove him back down to the boardinghouse where he was staying in Montego Bay.

I told him to be ready in a month and gave him some money as a retainer and a show of good faith. He hung out at the beach, spent the retainer, and stayed drunk waiting for my call. He was a friendly drunk.

The first crop had been growing for almost five months and was nearly ready to harvest when one hot, dry afternoon at the edge of a pungent field, Kit suddenly went into labor. She knew what was happening and communicated it through screams and yells to the women in the village. Kit was stoic, but winced and cried with each new wave of labor pain.

The other women moved with calm efficiency and produced a large bucket. They filled it with water and helped Kit lean against a banana tree and squat down over the critical bucket.

A sweaty and screaming few minutes later, our daughter

was born. The women knew how to cut the umbilical cord and clean the baby. When they brought her to us, wrapped in a clean blanket, Kit took her and we named her Indie, after the very first indica marijuana field in Jamaica, her birthplace. The world was going to be a new and different place for us all.

18 - JAMAICA JERK OFF

Indie was a month old when our first crop was ready to harvest. Thunder clouds rolled overhead, darkening the day, and the men worked quickly and efficiently to beat the rain. They didn't talk or kid one another. They worked with focus and me along with them.

Occasionally, thick, singular drops of rain fell on our bare arms and chests and tapped the leaves of the plants.

Fortunately, the rain held until the entire field was harvested and brought under a shelter where the women trimmed the plants. The storm lasted most of the night. In the morning, it was hot and clear.

High overhead, white clouds breezed by. I put on my shorts and went to look at the yield.

Clipped of their distinctly broad leaves, leaving only the dense purple buds clinging to leggy stalks, the plants were hanging upside down on wires. They would remain like that until they were dry enough to press into bricks without molding. The process took weeks. While we waited, we made manual presses to mash the weed flat once it was ready.

The yield was huge, about 1,800 pounds, and it was by far the most potent weed any of us - Ronnie, Winston, the growers, and Halsten - had ever smoked. It had a skunky smell and tasted sweeter than the tangy sativa that we were all accustomed to. The buzz was heavy and trance-like. It brought out the poet in Winston. He would get stoned and play reggae songs on his guitar for the children to sing. Ronnie would get more introspective than usual and would wander off to the creek by himself. The indica made me feel like a king, like the Lion of Judah that Winston always sang about. I felt like I knew who I was and what I was capable of accomplishing.

We loaded the dried and pressed weed onto the boat in duffle bags, boxes, and barrels. One of the growers, a guy named Calvin, went on the boat with Halsten, and they set off from Montego Bay for Miami with 1,800 pounds of weed and almost three years of work. Rather than risk arrest in the event of the worst, I flew to Miami on my own.

A couple of days before Halsten and Calvin landed, I made contact with the head of the Miami Parks and Recreation Department, a lanky, easily corruptible guy named Jake Whetmore. Normally, the gates to the public docks were chained and shut at ten o'clock at night. Under a heavy cash inducement, Whetmore agreed to personally arrive at one o'clock a.m., open the gates, and look the other way while I drove a rented van up to the docks at the ocean park.

Whetmore was right on time. Other than telling me to hurry it up, he didn't say much and, per our agreement, asked no questions. The boat was already there, and when I saw Halsten and Calvin step out of the cabin with four-day beards on their faces, I started laughing. I couldn't help it. I wasn't laughing because they looked bad, but because the plan was working, and I felt the rush that only comes from that.

Halsten and Calvin stayed with me in Miami, and we celebrated in the local fashion by doing coke off the fake tits of strippers. On my previous trip to Miami, I had briefed Dennis that his next load was going to include 1,800 pounds of Jamaican indica - the only weed of its kind anywhere.

"After that, we're only doing the weed," I told him.

"I don't think some of these guys are gonna want to

switch," he said. "You know how they are."

"Yeah, I know how they are. We might have to find some new guys, you know?" When I said "we", I really just meant him.

There was a pause. "Ok," he said. "No problem. I know some guys."

That was exactly the kind of attitude I wanted from the people I worked with. Assembling my team, I found people who were productive and who could make things happen on their own. I wasn't interested in trying to squeeze productivity out of somebody who was not productive, and some people just aren't. Dennis was.

For three weeks, Halsten, Calvin, and I stayed coked up in Miami until Dennis got back with the money. He had sold all the weed easily, and, though he did report some panicky noise from the more crack-addled dealers in regard to the dwindling coke business, most had agreed to buy the indica whenever it came through.

After Dennis got his cut, and Halsten was paid his exorbitant fifteen percent of the total, we ended up clearing 600 dollars a pound. Altogether, I made more than a million bucks from that first crop.

Dennis sold mostly to high-level dealers who bought hundreds of pounds at a time. They paid 1,200 dollars a pound because they could sell them for 2,000 dollars to mid-level dealers who would break the pounds down into ounces. In 1988, typically, an ounce of South American or Jamaican sativa sold for about eighty dollars an ounce. We sold our indica for 300. It was a crazy amount of money for an ounce of weed, but my weed was one of kind. There was nothing else like it anywhere.

I put most of my personal take - almost half a million dollars in cash - in my safe deposit box in Miami. I took back to Jamaica only what I needed to pay the crew and stock the farm. I paid each of the growers twenty dollars a pound per yield. At 1,800 pounds, each man stood to make 36,000 dollars on this yield. To a family of Rastas living in a hut on a pot farm, that was an almost incomprehensible amount of money. Everybody down the line was making money and getting high in a whole new way.

Departing Miami for Jamaica, I smuggled aboard a .22 caliber, six-shot revolver. I didn't tell Halsten about it only because he probably would have charged me another 10 percent. Ronnie, Winston, and I had discussed it one night and decided that a gun might be a good thing to have, just in case. Nobody else knew about it. When we got back to the farm, I tucked the pistol under the front seat of the truck and never said anything about it.

Morale was at a peak and the crew was inflated with self-esteem. They were proud of the high price that their product demanded. They bought shoes and clothes for their kids and themselves and long, bright dresses for their newly animated wives. The women bought pillows, cooking utensils, and spices. To everyone's delight, there was no more need to rely as extensively on so-so food.

Everybody was flush with cash, and spirits soared as we got our next crop in the ground and it started to sprout.

I decided to let the lease run out on the estate and bought a condo in Montego Bay, but my new family and I still chose to stay most nights in our hut in the valley. Kit and I delighted in Indie's development and her budding curiosity about the natural world around her. Kit would hold her and bathe her in the creek, and she would laugh and splash in the warm water.

Ronnie and Winston both moved to the farm. Winston built a hut not far from ours, but Ronnie didn't bother. He had the peculiar desire and ability to sleep outside without any type of shelter or covering. When we camped out as kids, back when he was 8 and I was 12, he never slept in the tent, unless it was raining. Cleanliness had never been a priority for him, and, as he settled into life on the farm, he went native with particular relish.

Like me, Ronnie had a chameleon-like quality. We were both able to adapt and blend into different situations easily. He was diligent and fearless at whatever task he faced with. He was at home wherever he happened to be, and he enjoyed himself heartily.

"One day is as good as the next to die," he said one evening when we were smoking a joint and looking at the new field of marijuana.

"That's a pretty morbid thing to say," I said, "What makes you say that?"

"I was just thinking that it only applies if you make every day a good day," he said.

"What are you talking about, man? Think of something cheerful," I said.

"I am being cheerful."

"Whatever, dude."

Ronnie's adventurous spirit belied a sad fatalism that was apparent, but not a thing we ever really discussed.

The crew on the farm accepted Ronnie as one of their own. He always understood, or seemed to understand what the men were arguing or joking about in their heavy dialect. I could leave the farm with Ronnie for weeks at a time when I went to Miami as required by business. He didn't have any bad habits that were liabilities. About once a month, he would go to Montego Bay and blow off steam with Halsten, who wore his sad fatalism on his sleeve, but Ronnie was totally reliable: a solid dude.

Winston was an excellent diplomat and a congenial go-between with local law enforcement and the religious leaders who held sway over the rural communities. We gave them regular "donations" for the privilege of growing our weed without hassle. Winston met with the police officials and re-negotiated the terms of our loose contract whenever necessary. Winston got us the crew and found the land, but Ronnie had his eye on everything at once.

A month into our second crop, everything, as I saw it, looked good. Jamaica is a strange and beautiful place. But I would learn that it can also be frighteningly unpredictable. Routine is a tentative abstract and order, where it exists, is easily unbalanced.

19 - JOHNNY TOO BAD

I went to Miami to do a routine coke deal and Ronnie was in Montego Bay drinking, hanging out at the beach, and doing whatever it was he did when he went down there by himself. I had just deposited 40,000 dollars in my safe deposit box and was back at the hotel doing lines, listening to Phil Collins, for old times sake, and planning my night when I got the call.

It was Winston and what he told me didn't sound real, as if it came from a nightmare. Indie had been kidnapped.

According to Winston, there was nothing anybody on the farm could do as a man with an automatic assault rifle and a demonic fire in his eyes called Bad Dog stuffed Indie, screaming, in the back seat of a battered BMW and sped out of the valley.

"Is everybody okay? How's Kit?" I asked, feeling numb and trying to suppress a rising panic.

"She's upset, but she's not hurt," said Winston, "Nobody is hurt, but they're scared."

"Who is this guy? His name is Big Dog? Why did - What does he want?" I asked. Questions were forming faster than I could spit them out.

"Bad Dog," corrected Winston, "He wants a ransom for the baby."

"What? How much?"

"He didn't say. It happened so fast. He just took her and drove away."

"I'm on my way."

I hung up and took the next flight to the Sangster International Airport in Montego Bay. It felt like no time at all before we were screeching to stop on the runway. Pounding waves of fear, anger, and hatred, catalyzed by the cocaine, boiled in my brain and had reduced the flight time to nothing. I shoved my way to the front of the plane and was first to get off.

A week later, journalistic accounts of a gangland mass-murder and a coke-crazed terror spree emerged. The gaps in the timeline immediately preceding the kidnapping of my daughter were filled in by word-of-mouth from those who survived.

Bad Dog was a hulking, dark-skinned, distant cousin of a small-time Kingston gangster named Afton. Bad Dog grew up in rank poverty in the country. As a desperate young man with nothing to lose, he learned to use his only natural asset, his size and fearsomeness, to commit strong arm robberies whenever he wanted something to eat other than what he scavenged from the hillsides and garbage cans.

He stalked the different villages around Montego Bay barefoot in his cut-off blue jeans and sweat-stained t-shirt, which were his only possessions. With belligerent fury as his default method of expression, he was a despised and fabled character in the villages. It was rumored that he had never owned a pair of shoes. To children who had never seen him, he existed as a pathetic, cautionary tale, and his name was invoked as a schoolyard insult.

With stolen money, he bought a one-way bus ticket to Kingston to pay his cousin Afton a visit. Afton and his pals lived in city apartments from which they dealt cocaine and fenced weapons and stolen goods. They wore jewelry, shiny shirts, sunglasses, slacks, and dress shoes. At night, they drove BMWs and Mercedes-Benzes to nightclubs where they drank liquor and spent lavishly. Theirs was a way of life at odds with old world superstitions of the hills and the relative strictures of Rastafarianism.

When Bad Dog arrived in Kingston, he talked his way into Afton's apartment. Afton had only a dim recollection of having met this ridiculous bumpkin when visiting his grandparents in the country, back when both men were small children, back when the malodorous, black Hercules standing in his apartment was still called Beaumont.

Afton figured that as long Bad Dog was going to hang around, he might as well not be offensive, so he told him to take a shower and loaned him something to wear from his expensive wardrobe. Next, the two cousins took the BMW and went shopping.

Bad Dog was awestruck by the amount of cash Afton spent and the degree of deference with which he was waited on and attended wherever they went. Afton enjoyed the admiration and his ego was gratified by the new experiences to which he exposed Bad Dog: eating in a restaurant, drinking champagne, buying shoes, and snorting coke.

That night, in Afton's apartment doing coke and smoking weed with him and his gang, Bad Dog's brain was boiling in new chemicals and conjuring new desires. The apartment was a repository of automatic weapons and cash. All of the men there, except Bad Dog, were carrying guns. They brandished them casually, not out of malice or threat, but for the sensation of moving the volatile mass through space and the thrill of its deadly potential. The air in the room was charged.

Bad Dog recognized and related to the uncompromising walk along the razor's edge that these men had chosen. He understood and appreciated their apparent disregard for risk and consequence.

Life was cheap and sensation could be deadly. The penalty in Jamaica for possession of even a bullet was death, and these men waved automatic weapons as if they'd been born holding them. Dub reggae boomed from Afton's elaborate sound system and marijuana smoke collected, in a dense, unmoving fog, at the ceiling.

With no warning or ripple in the collective unconsciousness of the doped young gangsters, they were surprised, and most of them killed instantly as a barrage of machine gun fire ripped through the door. A major crime syndicate had picked that night to assert its dominance in the local drug market.

Afton's friends, who survived the initial volley as he did, scrambled and fired their weapons blindly as they sought cover amid the exploding furnishings. Bad Dog had taken cover under a body and lay still while the gangsters screamed and their guns clapped out brutal fate. In seconds, the apartment and the people in it were reduced to worthless scraps. Then, there was stillness.

The acrid smell of burned powder hung in the air replacing the smell of marijuana. If anyone had survived, they were gone. The
high-pitched ring of sudden silence told Bad Dog it was time to act. Around him lay ten dead bodies, all wearing blood-soaked shiny shirts and hard soled shoes.

He quickly gathered all the money and coke he could cram in his pockets. He pulled a slippery AK-47 from the bloody hands of a dead boy who hadn't gotten a chance to fire it. Stepping over bodies and debris, he went to a spare bedroom where he had seen a stack of curved clips that matched the one in the AK-47. He grabbed one of them and came back in the living room. Afton was slumped against the wall with his neck at a peculiar angle. Bad Dog grabbed the keys to his BMW because he knew where it was parked. He didn't look back as he ran through the building and out to the street. Bad Dog was on his own again.

Police cars with crying sirens passed him going the opposite direction as he sped away. Driving too fast, barely handling his blind, last-second turns, Bad Dog made it out of Kingston. The damp, country air was still and smelled sweet. He pulled over on a narrow road and took the license plates off the car and flung them into the tall grass. His brush with underworld glamour ended as badly as it could have. What remained in Bad Dog was an appetite, not just for survival, but also for power.

He took up in a boardinghouse in a modest village and haunted its two bars. Running on residual adrenaline and incredibly pure cocaine, he conspicuously waved the stolen cash around and boasted in a loud, arrogant parody of Afton's glide through the Kingston afternoon.

When girls weren't as compliant as he preferred, Bad Dog would swear at them and smack them around. Even in the middle of a crowded bar, such brutality rarely raised contention. The girls just quit coming around.

After a couple of days, Bad Dog skipped out on his bill at the boardinghouse and took his routine to a more remote village, one without boarding houses and bars. The people there occupied themselves with toil and sheltered themselves in rickety shacks. More donkeys bumped along in the streets than motor vehicles, and those were mostly Honda motor bikes or pick up trucks from the 1940s.

Certainly, nothing like a brand new BMW 5 Series had ever come down the road and, certainly, not driven by a coked up fool shooting an AK-47 into the air. He startled the pack animals and farmers out of the streets.

Whoever could not, or symbolically would not, flee were victimized. He taunted and abused the women, along with the men, and kicked at the children. He would fire bursts from the rifle at nothing in particular and rob the petrified old people in the markets for what little they had.

Back in the BMW, he fired the gun out the window as he tore away with his meager spoils. Up the winding, unpaved country roads, he pushed the car's capacity for speed on such terrain. The village nearest my farm was the next place Bad Dog skidded to a stop.

Again, he terrorized people with the AK-47, firing it into the air to punctuate another pointless raid on the impoverished villagers and passive Rastas. After he had beaten and frightened what little money he could out of them, he made his way down to the farm.

Winston, Kit and Indie, the crew and their families were all at the farm when Bad Dog showed up. The closest things to weapons on the farm were the machetes. They were totally defenseless.

Bad Dog understood that the farm had value and, as such, it was a thing to be plundered and gutted. Just as there were no weapons on the farm, there was no cash, and, other than the acres of unripe marijuana plants, little else of black market value. He ransacked every hut in the valley in his search for something to steal. Upstream, he heard crying in the last and largest hut, and found the jewel of his deranged crime spree. He went in and emerged from my hut with Indie under one arm and bracing the AK-47 with other. He put her in the back of the car and tore out of the valley.

Two hours after getting Winston's call in Miami, I was in Montego Bay looking for Ronnie in his usual haunts. When I found him, he was getting drunk by himself in the colorful beachfront bar where I first met Halsten. I breathlessly told him what little I knew about Bad Dog and Indie.

The news seemed to sober him up. I drove us up to the farm in the truck. Getting there took another two hours of moving no faster than twenty-five miles-per-hour over unpaved roads through the godless bush. When we arrived, Kit was wrung out from her grief. I tried to console her, but she barely seemed to see or hear me from the bottom of her despair. She wept quietly in the consolation of the farm wives while Ronnie, Winston, and I gathered under a gas lantern in my hut.

"The only place he could hide is north. In the hills," said Winston, "In the jungle. He won't be in the village."

We got in the truck and Winston took the wheel. He knew every winding road and horse path through the dense hills. On a night so black, the land was disorienting and felt haunted. After bumping our way through two miles of dense jungle foliage, we found the BMW and parked behind it. From under the seat of the truck I grabbed the .22 pistol I had smuggled from Miami on the boat. It wasn't much of a gun, but it was better than nothing. I caught a brief look from Winston that let me know he was disappointed that I hadn't told him about it.

The three of us stood still and listened to the night. The sound of a baby crying came from the left and we went that way. My heart raced, as we crept slowly and silently, led by Indie's cries and Winston's dim flashlight. Through the tangled jungle, we saw the red light of Bad Dog's campfire ahead. His massive silhouette moved restlessly around it. The canopy of twisted branches that blocked the moonlight swallowed Indie's raw crying.

"Bad Dog!" I yelled from our position in the darkness. There was only the sound of crying. Nothing moved. "Bad Dog!"

This time, a quick rattle from the AK-47 answered me. We ducked. It was impossible to know how close the rounds came to hitting us.

"Who's there?" Bad Dog shouted and again fired a burst in our direction. "Answer me!"

"We're here for the baby! That's all we want!"

Bad Dog answered with incoherent profanity as another protracted blast from the AK-47 snapped branches and chipped tree bark above our heads. Then, the clatter stopped. Indie wailed. Bad Dog cursed again, but this time quietly to himself. When another moment passed this way, we knew the clip was empty. Bad Dog was out of bullets.

We leapt from our cover and charged toward Bad Dog's camp.

He was on the other side of the fire holding Indie and frantically hammering the trigger of the useless assault rifle.

He waved it and yelled, "Stay back! Stay away!" The shiny patterned shirt he wore was ripped and stained; his hard soled shoes were caked with dirt.

Holding the .22 out in front of me, I moved around the fire flanked by Ronnie and Winston. Bad Dog backed away, fading into the moonless horror of the jungle. Without saying anything, as automatically as swatting a fly, I shot him in the knee. His bloodshot eyes flashed and his white teeth snapped in agony. He dropped Indie, staggered backward, and fell. Ronnie and Winston immediately closed on him and I picked up Indie. Tucking her head under my chin, I held her tight to my pounding chest.

Ronnie and Winston beat Bad Dog until he quit struggling. His breath was still coming, but just barely. Ronnie bent the barrel of the AK-47 and left it there with Bad Dog and the dying fire.

20 - ROLL WITH IT

After Indie's kidnapping, I had a better understanding of the limits of my payouts to the local law enforcement, such as there were. The coverage obviously didn't include protection against kidnapping or being threatened with a machine gun. Instead, my payouts were interpreted as gifts and signs of respect and good faith rather than a fee for protection, as it was with Jake Whetmore of the Miami Parks and Recreation Department.

Clubs and ancient six-shot revolvers were the only weapons carried by the rural Jamaican sheriffs, and they were as scared of Bad Dog as the defenseless villagers that they were sworn to protect.
Common sense and cowardice trumped principle and justice. I had no choice, but to accept that as the way of things. I was a costly lesson and, once learned, I was determined that it would never cost anymore than it already had.

Individually, the local police weren't as ineffectual as they were as a collective body. As long as there was nothing for them to do, they were decent enough guys. Like the Rastafari leaders, they liked our weed and wanted the farm to be successful and make money, and they wanted that money to circulate in the village. They thought our operation was a good thing, but they weren't willing to die violent deaths at the hands of a coke-up psychopath defending it. Who could blame them? They were as motivated by self-interest as anybody else I ever dealt with.

With the novelty of rustic farm life expired, Kit and Indie started staying in the condo in Montego Bay all the time. I stayed with them there most nights, but I would get more restless than the occasional late night with Halsten, if he wasn't with a woman, or Ronnie if he was around, could satisfy. The heat, the camaraderie, the work, and the atmosphere of growth and vitality at the farm energized me. In the field, under the Jamaican sun, I was ageless. I felt as if I were plugged into a battery. I missed it when I was away for too many days. Being on the farm less, I tried to make my time there count more.

I met in a middle-aged guy in Montego Bay named Don. He wore Hawaiian shirts and Italian loafers and worked for a film distributor shipping first-run movies around the Caribbean. He would be in town for a few days every month, and I started having drinks with him now and then. We had some common interests, getting stoned and watching movies among them, so I contracted with him to bring a movie to the farm once a month and show it for everybody.

"Come up any Saturday night that works best for you," I proposed.

"What about when the movie's over and it's dark?" he said. "I can't leave the screen and the rig there."

"You can stay the night. It's like camping," I said even though Don didn't look like a camper.

He looked at me impassively over the tops of his glasses and said nothing.

"I've got a generator and some flood lights," I said taking another tack, "And a crew. The crew will help you."

For a thousand dollars and a half-pound of fresh indica, he agreed.

I was to drive Don, the film, and all the necessary projection equipment up into the hills, through the bush to the valley, and then drive him back when the show was over.

"Is it much further?" Don asked as we made our rough way through the hills on our first movie night. "Will we be meeting up with the road again?"

I could tell that he was nervous for his safety as well as that of the precious film cans, property of a powerful media conglomerate which he was feloniously trafficking and exhibiting for a profit. He relaxed once we pulled into the valley and he saw the manicured rows of marijuana plants bathing in the late afternoon sun. He was impressed by the workmanship of the tidy huts and shelters on the property.

I introduced him around, and we smoked a couple of large spliffs waiting for the sun to set. By the time it was dark enough to watch the movie, Don was so stoned he could barely instruct the crew how to set up the screen.

First, a seven-foot-tall framework needed to be erected and stabilized. A screen made of thick, silver fabric was then draped over the frame and fastened in place along the top and bottom.

"Try to remember this," I said to the crew, mostly for Don's benefit, "You have to do it again, in reverse, in the dark." I laughed, but nobody else did.

The projector and sound system went on top of a rig that he set up in the bed of the truck. Once everything was wired to the generator, we smoked more weed and waited for sundown.

Once it got dark, it was show time. The feature that night was *Rambo III*. Rambo goes to Afghanistan to rescue his old Colonel who's been kidnapped. It was great. I asked Ronnie if this was what his trip to Afghanistan was like. This time I got some appreciative chuckles, but not from him.

"I wish," he said.

We harvested the second crop and I put Halsten on-point: as soon as the weed was dried and pressed, it would be time for another big Miami run. The yield was another 1,800 pounds. Calvin, who proved to be as bright and able a seaman as he was a farmer, went with Halsten, and I decided go on the boat this time to keep costs down, and it seemed like fun.

We checked into the same hotel as before. When I met Dennis, he paid for 900 pounds, half the load, and I fronted him the other half. That way, we didn't have to wait around to get paid. He drove the bricks of weed away from the dock in a rumbling, ten-foot box truck.

The Miami nightlife mysteriously held less appeal for us this time. I met Jorge and he gave us some free coke, but it just made me edgy. Calvin got high and became consumed with anxiety and obsessed with trivial details, and Halsten drank like he was trying to put himself to sleep. Somehow, he managed to provoke a valet into punching him in the nose. I never learned the reason for that. We returned to the hotel suite resolved to leave in the morning as soon as we were able.

The three-day trip back to Montego Bay was smooth and the azure sky was pure and clear. Still, we sailed under a shadow we couldn't define, nor did we try. We spoke little and were quick to be agreeable and accommodating when we did.

When we docked at the marina in Montego Bay, it was with a shared sense of relief. The trip wasn't nearly as much fun as I had hoped it would be. I fully realized what I felt in my heart all along that the growing and selling of the weed was not nearly as stressful as the smuggling of it. Still, I felt it was important to participate directly in every aspect of the business and show my team that I never asked them to do anything that I wasn't willing to do myself.

Calvin and I parted ways with Halsten and waited in the

bar for Ronnie to pick us up in the truck. As we drank our beers, the cloud that had settled over us in Miami began to lift. When Ronnie showed up in the truck, we were in a brighter mood. We bought food for the month and took it to the farm. Everyone was happy to see us and we celebrated a successful second crop.

It was even more potent than our first crop. The growers had started cloning the female plants, and there were several dozen
five-gallon buckets placed all around the farm, each containing a compact blue-green plant that was almost all bud. The local villagers and the Miami kingpins alike said it was the best weed they had ever smoked, and they were some of the most stoned people on Earth.

21 - WHITE CLIFFS OF DOVER

On a hot Sunday in the fall, when the third crop was nearing maturity, Kit and some of the other women took some of the children to go swimming at a waterfall in the mountains. Carnell, one of the growers, knew the way and volunteered to make the rocky, treacherous drive up the mountain when Winston begged off. Indie stayed with me and we dozed and played in the hut. The women and most of the children piled into the bed of the truck and it slowly rumbled away. The day was bright and the air was still.

A couple of lazy hours passed when the yellow sunlight quickly faded, and the world outside my hut turned grey. I went outside to take a look. In the span of a few seconds, the temperature dropped noticeably. Heavy piles of low black and grey clouds tumbled over the mountain darkening the valley. Winston and the crew were also watching the ominous transformation overhead and warning the children who were still there inside to safety. No superstition or stiffness in the joints, which is how most weather predictions on the farm were made, had forecast what came next.

Heavy drops of dark rain thumped the ground and slapped the leaves on the trees for a moment, and then the drops increased. All at once, hard wind and driving rain whipped the valley and obliterated any other sound and vision. Thunder cracked like artillery fire and rattled the huts.

Sudden summer thunderstorms are a ubiquity in the southeastern United States. They rage mightily and blow over quickly, but the Jamaican variety was proving to be something more protracted and severe. It was a remorseless thrashing with intensity beyond the measure of my experience.

I might not have been quite as uneasy if Indie and Kit had been safely inside the hut with me. I could soothe Indie if she were frightened by the thunder and help her understand that storms are a part of life as perfect and temporary as the good fortunes of the sun. I hoped that wherever they were on the mountain they were safe.

The roof of my hut was leaking in three places. No matter how I positioned myself, it was impossible for some part of me not to be under at least one of them. Gradually, the fury of the rain diminished, but it continued to fall steadily. It was the kind of rain that endures. The sky lightened to an even, medium grey.

I covered myself with a tarp and went to look at the crop. It had taken a beating. I saw stalks broken in half and long branches and broad leaves littering the field. Some plants were bent in the middle and slumped against the others. I sighed and turned away. There was nothing else I could do.

The plants that were standing, at least, were still alive. I thought maybe some of the larger branches could be repotted and cloned in buckets. It wasn't a disaster, but it was a dispiriting thing to see on top of my concern for Kit and the others on the mountain. I laid down in my hut, tried in vain to stay out of the drips, and listened to the rain. I thought about rolling a joint, just for something to do, but I didn't.

I don't know how long I laid there before Carnell drove slowly down the hill in the rain with a truck full of drenched women and children. A feeling of relief came over me like a hot bath. I grabbed my tarp and ran to meet them.

As soon as the truck stopped the children jumped out of the back and ran to their huts. A woman got out of the cab of the truck crying. I didn't see Kit. Carnell came around the front of the truck and his eyes told me before he did: Kit was dead.

Carnell explained through his tears that the way to the waterfall was blocked, and they had already started back to the valley when the storm broke. They had no choice, but to stop where they were, on a narrow road running along the face of a cliff. The truck slid on the flooded road, and Kit fell out of the back.

I took Indie and went back to my hut. Ronnie ran over when he heard. He hugged me and said how sorry he was and that he would do anything he could for me. I told him I knew it was true and asked him to drive Indie and me to the condo in Montego Bay. I wanted her to sleep in her bed, in her home, out of the rain.

Ronnie stayed with us. There weren't two other people that I would rather have been with on that miserable night. They were the two people to whom I was closest in the world, one by blood and the other by something better.

Early the next morning, we left Indie with Winston and Ronnie, and I went back to recover Kit's body. The funeral was filled with songs and tears. My love was buried on the farm.

Only Ronnie knew who I really was. To all the people I had dealt, drugged, and slept with in the past three years I was Steven Jones. Not Kit, Winston, Halsten, or any of the crew knew my real name.

I didn't sleep that night. The bed didn't feel like mine. I hadn't slept in it enough when Kit was there to share it with me. Even when I was there, it hadn't truly been me. Now, it might as well have been a stone slab. Alone, I didn't know who I was. That didn't excuse my responsibility to my two-year-old daughter. Existential pondering was a comfort I didn't deserve.

22 - PATIENCE

Relying on my ability to adapt, I started trying to get used to life with Indie and without Kit. The third harvest recovered from the storm and, though it was delayed, we didn't lose any weight due to the buds we were cloning in the buckets. The crew had moved most of those under cover before the storm.

In terms of quality, we had again outdone ourselves. The buds were bigger and denser than ever before. We were honing the skills and trying, for what it was worth, to understand and harmonize with the atmospheric rhythms of the valley. It worked more than it didn't, but nothing came easy.

Halsten, Calvin and I took the third harvest to Miami as we had before. This time the pall that had descended on us a few months ago was gone. All Calvin brought with him was a hardback book that was about three inches thick. He was stretched out shirtless on the deck.

"What are you reading?" I asked.

"*Anna Karenina*," he said and showed me the cover, his finger marking his place, "By Tolstoy."

"Tolstoy huh? Is it any good?"

"I just started it," he said and re-opened the book to continue

reading.

We all enjoyed the cruise. The weather was cool and clear, and once we landed the boat we were in good spirits. When I met up with Dennis, he paid me what he owed me on the last load - half a million dollars. He also told me he had a connection with a south-Florida biker gang that was interested in getting in the loop for some real weight.

Ordinarily, Dennis handled all that stuff himself. That was his business and I stayed out of it as long as the money made sense in the end. But, being a south-Florida biker gang, they were strange, violent paranoids and prone to territorial pissing of a most anti-social variety, and they wanted to meet me in person. So I had Dennis arrange a meeting.

Emmet's BBQ was a big restaurant and bar in Fort Lauderdale that catered to vacationing families in the evenings. It had a dining room downstairs and an open-air bar above it that faced the ocean. I was up there waiting for Dennis and his friend to arrive. It was late afternoon, not yet happy hour, and there weren't many people in the bar. A jukebox playing Aerosmith and Van Halen songs made most of the noise.

Since spending more time in Montego Bay after Kit's death, I tried to present myself as a responsible parent and not a pot farmer. I fell back on a personal style that dated to my fraternity days: Lacoste polo shirts in loud colors, khaki pants, Sperry top-siders, and no socks. It was the perfect look to clearly convey predictability and respectability.

Across the bar was grubby little guy with a ratty beard and heavily tattooed forearms wearing a leather vest. The way he pounded beers at a high and consistent rate, and the way he was increasingly belligerent in ordering subsequent rounds certainly fit my image of an outlaw biker, but Dennis was supposed to introduce me to my guy. That was the plan, and I figured I had nothing to lose by being patient and playing it straight.

I sipped my rum and Coke and pretended to watch the television, but I was aware that the little tough guy across the bar was staring at me intently. I was supposed to notice it, but I didn't let on that I had.

I looked at my watch. Dennis was twenty minutes late, which was extremely unusual for him. I was beginning to wonder how much longer it was going to be a good idea to hang around.

The bearded guy in the leather vest got off his stool and announced loudly to no one and everyone, "I gotta piss."

He was drunk and didn't notice, or didn't care about, the embarrassed and annoyed reactions of the bartender and the small handful of patrons. In heavy motorcycle boots, he stomped in an uncoordinated way to the restrooms.

When he went in, the bartender said to me, "Man, he's loaded.

I need to need cut him off, but I'm kind of afraid to."

"Is he a regular or something?" I asked.

"I've never seen him before, but he's a real asshole." The bartender went back to his happy-hour prep, cutting limes and whatnot.

I took another sip of my drink and looked at my watch again. The restroom door banged open and the drunk guy stormed out. He came around the bar and stood right behind me. My body tensed and I didn't move. I wasn't going to let some drunk goad me into a fight when I was there to make a 100,000 dollar dope deal. I just stayed still.

I couldn't help but flinch when I felt the guy's oily beard slowly brushing the back of my neck, back and forth. My skin crawled and I could hear my pulse surging through my head. I could feel his breath in my hair as he rubbed his beard from one side of my bare neck to the other. Back and forth.

I had no idea what to do. I was grinding my teeth trying not to give any reaction while my brain spun in high gear. I had a pocketknife, but I wasn't going to stab anybody at Emmet's BBQ just before happy hour, and I had to assume that this guy wouldn't hesitate to do that to me if threatened. Also, I still wasn't sure that this wasn't the very guy I was there to meet. His beard was still going back and forth across my neck. The bartender looked mortified and said nothing.

Back and forth, back and forth. Just as I was about to explode, Dennis walked in the bar. "Hey! Sorry I'm late," he said ignoring the bizarre scene that was taking place. "You two have met. Great! So, what are we doing?"

The dirty little biker just laughed and slapped me on the back. "Man, I'm sorry," he said.

After all, it was a short beard he had. It wasn't like it was a long beard.

Creepy feelings notwithstanding, a deal was reached with the bearded molester, who went by Fast Freddy, and the biker gang he represented. After that, I was free to enjoy the rest of the weekend with Calvin and Halsten without obligation.

Calvin, absorbed in his reading, stayed away from the nightclubs and cocaine this trip. Each morning he went to the beach and swam in the ocean, read, and napped on the warm sand. Even though I was technically single again, I left the whores to Halsten. Other than that, I unwound with the usual Miami vices.

Early Monday morning at the dock, we were hungover and sore, except Calvin who was stretched out on his back on the deck of the boat reading. The trip to Montego Bay was, thankfully, uneventful.

When we returned to the farm, we celebrated with everyone by sharing a huge dinner and enormous spliffs.

The mood was light. Months of challenge and pain were behind us and we had every reason to feel good. Cloned buds were hanging and drying, and the next crop was already planted in the fields. But without Kit, the joy was compromised and diminished. I missed the final validation that she offered with her love.

My back and head ached when I emerged from my hut in the morning. The farm looked different to me. It was more successful than ever, but the allure of the eternal camping trip had faded. The creek looked dirty and I didn't want Indie to get in it. The communal areas of the farm, where the crew would kick the soccer ball and the children would play, looked worn and muddy. In the tall, uniform rows of marijuana plants, the first of their kind in that part of the world, I saw stewardship and accomplishment, and I was proud of it, but as I went downstream to piss in the creek, I knew the farm was coming to an end. Just as surely as prices would rise, the farm wouldn't last forever.

Once he was up, I had Ronnie drive Indie and me to the condo.

"How do you think it's going?" I asked.

"I think it's going great," Ronnie said evenly, looking ahead at the bumpy road. "Everybody's got money. The crew is happy."

"You ever think about what you're gonna do next?" I said.

For a moment, Ronnie didn't say anything, he just handled the truck. "I know what you mean," he said, "And no. I don't really think about what comes next."

I watched him drive. "You don't, do you?"

Never one to waste words, he didn't say anything, and I didn't know how he really felt. He acted the way I expected him too, and, in his mute consistency, I took some small comfort.

23 - WHAT'D I SAY

I was I born natural at language and dialect. When I was a child playing with toy cars while Effie did the ironing, I would listen to her words and enunciation and talk back to her the same way. Her nephews would come over to play and I would ask them to say the words that they would use to go up to the back of the house and knock and call for Effie.

Raymond the pudgy one said "I know what I'd say."

"What?" I asked.

"I'd say, 'Aunt Effie, Aunt Effie I want a piece of chocolate cake

please.'"

"Say that over and over until I've got it down to a T." I said. We practiced and practiced. I knew I had it right when their mouths fell open.

The next day when Effie was in the house, I went out the front door and circled around to the back. I waited and practiced the words. I knocked and like magic the words came out. Effie said, as she walked through the house, "Raymond, what are you doin' here? Hold on, hold on. I'll get you a piece of chocolate cake. No wonder you're so damn fat." She got the cake and came out to the back door. "Well Steven, where's Raymond?"

"When you said he was fat, he ran off. But I'll take the cake."

As a kid, I had no problem hearing and understanding the words and what they meant when I was walking the Big 9. When mom once caught me talking to Effie when I was 5 years old, she took me to my room and said, "Honey, it's impolite for a white person to talk colored to a black person. You're white, Stevie. And you'll be starting school soon and at school they speak white."

"Okay mama."

She spun around and said, "Mama, mama, mama. I'm not your mama I'm your mother, understood?"

Oh well, from then on I guarded my gift.

In the 4th, 5th, and 6th grades I took German Language from a real German, Jens Kappei. In his class, I spoke German just exactly as he spoke, when he spoke English with a German accent, I spoke it just like him.

Before Bobby and Johnny moved to Panama they lived up North and they were yankees. So for two weeks in the winter and two weeks in the summer, I spoke yankee.

After meeting Jorge, I thought Spanish might really help, so I took Spanish my sophomore, junior, and senior years. On every trip to Panama Ms. Garcia would tell me how much I had improved.

One night years later, when Jorge and I were partying in Miami, I bet him $10,000 that I could call TK and TJ, and they would not know it was me and not him.

"Jorge what would you say and how would you say it to get them to come over now?" He spoke to me and I said, "Again and again - I got it, Just the right dialect." I called the guys and they were both over in 15 minutes. Good bet. Up until then, TK and TJ did not know that I could speak Spanish.

Then, when the Woodstock Five moved in, they only spoke Latin in the house. It was their way to honor and keep alive a dead language. No problem, I learned Latin just to piss them off. I got quite good and could speak and understand every word they said in that house, unless they talked really fast or used Latin incorrectly.

Indie was 2 ½ Years old when Kit died. The first thing I did was get her out of diapers and into big girl panties. The next thing was to get her some education. At the farm she spoke patois, a form of Jamaican-slang-English, with the children in the village. At the condo in Montego Bay, she spoke proper English with Winston, and when Indie and I were alone we spoke Latin. After Kit died, Indie and I spent more time at the condo in Montego Bay with Winston. Ronnie ran the farm.

When Indie and I would drive to the farm we would practice Latin. It was a two hour drive one way, so we had plenty of
father-daughter time. We spoke Latin and played "who are we gonna be" games. Indie would pretend to be a princess. She would say, in Latin, "Ego sum null princeps Alice." I was a knight by the name of David. We had to stay that way all day. Each trip we used different names, and we tried to be as creative as we possibly could. Indie was always better at it than I was. *Cras nos volo exsisto quispiam alivs*, she would say: tomorrow we will be someone else.

Latin formed a bond between Indie and me. It was our secret language. When she could not say what she wanted to say in English, usually because of other people in the room, she would talk to me in Latin. Really cool for a four year old girl.

24 - I DON'T WANT TO MISS A THING

Indie was 4 ½ years old when she got sick. She had a cough and fever with weight loss. I wanted her to be treated by a doctor in the United States, in order to receive the best care. I tired to fly her to Miami, but she was too sick, and they would not let her board the plane. Halsten had gotten himself in a scrape with a woman in Montego Bay who accused him of trying to buy drinks on her tab, so he was happy to get away and take us to Miami in the boat.

"You can go back whenever you want to, Halsten," I said when we docked. "I don't know how long this will take."

I carried Indie onto American soil. At the hospital, a licensed medical professional examined her for the first time in her life. She had never been inoculated or vaccinated for anything. Indie was admitted and x-rays revealed a ring in the lung. The doctor diagnosed her with tuberculosis, which would require hospitalization. She was very sick.

I blamed myself for her illness. The farm was unsanitary. I was her father, Indie was my daughter. At the hospital, I could not stay in the room with her. She was upset and had to use the bathroom. The nurse who was from rural Arkansas and was black, could not understand the patois that Indie thought surely she would understand. So Indie spoke proper English too fast which got her nowhere. At last Indie started trying Latin just as a young doctor was making his rounds. Indie started speaking Latin.

"Ego requirere tenus utur paitibus toilet. Pater, pater!"

"Doctor Long I can't understand a thing this girl is sayin'." The nurse said.

"She wants to go to the bathroom and then she wants to see her father, now. That, nurse, was Latin." the doctor said. "I want to see this girl's father as well."

I met with Dr. Long and he wanted to test me for TB. I asked about Indie, and he said he would place me in a glass room next to Indie's. With the drapes pulled back, we could see each other. When I went in that room, I did not realize that I would not be coming out. Just like Indie, I was quarantined. I'm not sure who cried more, me or Indie.

Luckily, I tested negative for tuberculosis, and, after 48 hours, I was allowed to leave. It would be three weeks before I could touch Indie and one more week before we could leave the hospital. During that time, I had Winston bring a contagious disease doctor to the farm and test everyone there, including Halston. Only one girl tested positive, and I paid for her treatment.

Indie had only one ring on her lung and would not have much long term damage. But she would require antibiotic maintenance drugs for the rest of her life. That trip cost $30,000 to Dade General and $10,000 for the doctor at the farm.

Doctor Long was interested in Indie and why she talked in Latin. "It's our secret language, our bond." I said. I explained that Indie's mother had died in an accident when Indie was 2 ½ years old, and that I had not married her mother. Indie's name was Indie Jones and my name was Steven James. I had a Jamaican birth certificate for Indie that we had gotten from a local doctor a day after Indie was born and had it registered in Kingston to make it official.

I told him that I needed Indie to have dual citizenship. He said he would help us as long as I was a U.S. Citizen. I was and I had proof, very seldom seen, and used even less, my real ID, driver's license, social security card, and birth certificate. I filled out forms, and Dr. Long put me in front of the right judge, and, by the time Indie could leave the hospital, she had her U.S. Citizenship papers. Thanks, Doc.

I had plenty of cash on hand to cover Indie's hospitalization however long it lasted. The doctor said she was making great progress and that she could be discharged within a week. I had that long to comes to terms with what I knew to be true: the next crop of marijuana would be my last. It was time to wind it down. While certainly easier than getting it started, quitting the pot business would also require some planning and finesse.

With Indie's dual-citizenship finally secure, we flew back to Jamaica just as the fourth crop was ready to harvest. I told Halsten to be prepared. He said he would be ready when the weed was. Then, he took the boat on a shakedown cruise and sank it.

"Sank it?" I screamed. "You're kidding me."

He was standing on the dock wearing his sunglasses and still dripping wet as he explained himself.

"I hit a reef," he said stoically.

"You didn't see it?"

The answer was obvious and Halsten didn't say anything. He just stood there and dripped. After a minute, he told me that the boat sank quickly and completely, near enough to shore for him to swim to the dock.

"Who knows about it?" I asked.

"I don't know," he shrugged, "Maybe nobody."

"What do we do, just leave it down there?"

"Yeah," he said, "I guess so."

We stood there in silence another minute.

Then he added, "I'm sorry I sank the boat. I misjudged the depth."

"I know," I sighed. "We can't do anything about it now."

Halsten nodded.

I listened to the sea birds' call, and the pulse of the ocean. The sunset was a brilliant orange streaked by fast-moving pink and purple clouds.

"Well," I said, "Let's go get a beer."

The crop was completely dried, cured, and pressed, ready for export, but without a boat, we were stuck with it. We rented a warehouse by the docks and kept the weed there. Winston, Ronnie, and I, and especially Halsten who was eager to redeem himself, searched diligently up and down the coast for a suitable boat to buy, similar to the one we lost. We didn't have two years to find it this time, not with a ton of the most expensive marijuana in the world sitting in a warehouse. That problem was quickly nullified by an even bigger problem.

The weed vanished. The warehouse had been broken into and our entire crop was stolen. With it went the salary for the crew and the expenses for the rest of the year.

"We gotta get whoever did this," I said pacing around the condo while Ronnie, Winton, and Halsten sat around the dining room table.

"You don't want to start acting like a cowboy now," said Ronnie passing a joint to Winston.

"Yes, I sure as hell do," I said.

"Whoever took it is probably long gone," said Winston, who was also not in favor of violent reprisal. He took a deep toke. "Nothing else was taken form the warehouse, just the weed. If they knew what it was, then they knew to get it out of here fast." He exhaled. "Everybody would recognize our weed."

"Everybody on that dock is a thief," reasoned Halsten. "They come and they go. It could have been anybody," he said swinging his glass of rum back and forth.

They were right, and it made me more ready than ever to be finished with the marijuana business.

"Where are we on finding a boat?" I asked.

Halsten was staring down to the bottom of his drink.

"Halsten!" I said getting his attention, "What about a boat, man?"

"Nothing," he said, "There's nothing."

I hit the joint twice. "Now, I gotta tell the crew," I sighed.

That conversation was as unruly and combative an exchange as you would expect from a group of farmers that were accustomed to a lavish income. I said I would subsidize them until another crop was done. They had fulfilled their end of the bargain, and the theft wasn't their fault. Paying them was the decent thing to do, but I can't say I was happy about it. In a three-week span, I lost a 300,000-dollar boat and a million dollars in weed.

Since I was a shirtless, sweaty teenager running through the fields in Panama, I wanted to find a perfect place of my own to grow marijuana in the open air. I wanted to find the right climate, not just in terms of the weather, but also an agreeableness with the people and the place itself.

For the past five-and-a-half years, Jamaica was that place.

Throughout most of that time, I felt at home. The local law enforcement was nothing to depend on, but they were also nothing to worry about. Happy with my donations, they and the influential religious leaders ignored us, for better and for worse. The villagers, on the other hand, loved us because we spent money.

I had been allowed to stand in the perfect spot, where the water, the earth, and the sun all coordinated, enabling me to grow the best outdoor marijuana in the world. By the bearings of my old-South heritage, I had long held a vision of myself as a plantation boss. I saw myself as the benevolent master, a steward of the land, an employer, and a leader. In Jamaica, my vision had been realized. But the wheel had turned, the land was now demanding that I fight to maintain the dominance I had struggled to establish.

Ghosts swept down the mountain at night and gathered on the shore whispering, "You do not know as much as you think you do." I heard their voices in my sleep, but I knew that when I left Jamaica it would be as a victor.

Veni, vidi, vici: I came, I saw, I conquered.

25 - I'M YOUR CAPTAIN

"Who are you?"

"I'm Rambo, who are you?"

"Miss Piggy."

Indie and I were playing her favorite game: pretending.

The sliding door to the terrace was open and the breeze carried in a sense of the sunny beach. The phone rang.

"Excuse me, Miss Piggy," I said and picked up the phone. It was Halsten with good news.

Before we planted the new crop, I told Winston that it would be my last. We were sitting on the tailgate of the pick-up truck one evening looking at a field of freshly tilled soil. I told him that after I sold the weed, I was out of the business and moving back to the U.S. with Indie. I offered him ownership of the farm, free and clear.

"What am I going to do with it?" said Winston, "I can't move that much weed. This takes organization," he said and gestured toward the field. "I can't do what you do."

"You'll do it your own way," I said.

"I don't want to," he said keeping his eyes fixed in the distance. "I'm going to Kingston."

"What are you going to do there?"

"Maybe I'll be a caretaker somewhere, or work in someone's house again," he said. "I'm good at that. It's what I like."

"Man, you're good at this. Keep doing this and you'll own a house, a nice one. You've been to my place-"

"My niece is in Kingston," he said cutting me off, still looking across the field. "Kit's first daughter."

After a moment I said, "I forgot about her."

Winston nodded. "I didn't forget," he said

"What is this, man? Why are you bummed out. This is a good thing. We did a good thing here."

He nodded again, but didn't rise to my enthusiasm.

"It's not done," he said. Again, he pointed at the newly sown field. "It's just starting. Starting over again."

This time I just nodded.

"Who else knows?" he said looking at me.

"Just Ronnie. I haven't told the crew, or Halsten."

Winston looked back out at the field. "Has he found a boat?"

"Yeah. He called me yesterday. I'm supposed to look at it tomorrow after I tell the crew."

The next morning, I gathered the crew together before they went to plant the field and told them that this would be the last crop.

"I'm gonna leave the farm to Indie. The land will be deeded to her officially, but you can keep the farm going and sell your crops here or try to bring them to the States, it's up to you, but you'll be on your own." I let what I said sink in and added, "Thank you, for everything."

They took the news in stride. This wasn't anybody's first job on a weed farm, except mine, and it was the best weed farm in the world. I didn't have to impress upon the men the importance of making this crop the best it could possibly be. Where I didn't think it was possible, they tended the young crop with more love than ever before.

Halsten was pacing on the dock when I met him to look at the boat that he found. It was a fifteen-year-old, thirty-eight-foot trawler yacht, with five berths and two diesel engines. Halsten liked it, saying he had driven one like it from the Isle of Youth to the Caymans years before, back when this boat was new.

I talked the seller, a sixty-eight-year-old tax fugitive with skin like saddle leather, down to 225,000 dollars, which Halsten assured me was a steal. When I paid the man, he told me that he liked my style. He had sunglasses on, but I could see him wink when he took my gym bag full of cash, and his teenage girlfriend handed Halsten the keys and the title to the yacht. Truly, it wasn't made for transporting much more than people. Its main assets were that it was a boat and it was ours.

On the morning of the last harvest, I went to the farm to get high one more time and to see the valley full and ripe. I wanted to remember it at its peak. The flowers on the plants were covered in sticky crystals, as if they had been rolled in diamond dust. The fields sparkled in the early sun.

Thanking the crew again for their effort, their professionalism, and their friendship, I said goodbye. When they went to work swinging their machetes, and the plants snapped and fell over, I went back to the condo at Montego Bay and held Indie in my lap. From the terrace, I watched the ocean roll in and recede. I concentrated on the rhythm of it. Indie was pretending to be somebody, some cartoon character I had never heard of. I couldn't play along just then.

That day was the last time I saw the farm. The next time I saw the weed was a month later in the middle of the night on the dock. It had been dried and pressed into tightly wrapped bricks. We had 1,800 pounds to stash. Loading the boat involved first tearing it apart to make room to hide it all. In preparation, we had spent the past few weeks gutting the boat at night. We pulled up the bottom so we could line the hull with weed. Care had to be taken to ensure that everything would fit back together and not look like it was bursting at the seams.

The plan worked, and once the boat was reassembled, there was no sign of the 1,800 pounds. From the outside, it was just another yacht. The inside, however, looked like a condemned Palm Beach hotel suite, a ruined suggestion of its former, gaudy opulence.

I left Indie in Winston's care at the condo and told her I would be back soon. The boat crew was the same: Halsten, Calvin, and me. At dawn, we sailed, with an excitement that verged on anxiety.

We had always been graced with good luck on the sea when it counted. There was no reason to think that this cruise would be any different, but the stakes were higher this time, and we were wired.

Calvin acted like he was reading a book, but he kept getting distracted. He would end up sitting with his finger marking his place and joining in conversation with Halsten and me.

"*Crime and Punishment*?" I said looking at Calvin's book, "That's not the right spirit. Why can't you read *Tom Sawyer* or something like that? *Treasure Island*?"

"It's about a murder," Calvin said without expression.

"Well, whatever, it's pretty morbid reading material for this kind of mission, don't you think?"

He just shrugged. It was almost over anyway. The Florida Keys were in sight.

"Calvin!" Halsten called from the cabin. We looked up. He was waving for Calvin to come in. After a couple of minutes, I went up to see what they were talking about. Just as I got to the cabin door, Calvin burst out and rushed below.

Halsten offered no explanation, and I was determined to assume everything was fine unless told otherwise.

"What's up?" I said to Halsten casually. "Where's that *Playboy* you were looking at earlier? I wanted to take a look at it."

"Right there," he said and pointed behind him with his thumb.

I picked up the magazine and started flipping through it.

"I asked Calvin to look at the engines," said Halsten, "It feels sluggish."

"What does? The boat?"

I looked down at the instrument panel with the ridiculous assumption that if something were wrong I would be able to decipher it from the dials and gauges. I tried to detect a feeling of sluggishness, but it felt to me as though we were cruising along steadily. It was impossible to determine Halsten's level of concern through his sunglasses.

Suddenly, Calvin appeared wide-eyed and breathless at the cabin door.

"The bottom is full of water," he said.

Halsten and I looked at him.

"I think it's sinking."

I turned to Halsten. "You son-of-a-bitch, did you sink another one of my boats?"

"I don't think so. We didn't hit anything," he said, his voice rising.

I pushed past Calvin and bounded below decks where it smelled faintly of diesel exhaust. A deep pool of water was slowly spreading from the back right corner of the hull. Calvin had exaggerated a bit, the bottom wasn't full, but the situation was critical.

"Quick! Get the pumps going," I said to Calvin who was standing behind me.

By the time the pumps were running, water was flowing into the hull. The breach, wherever it was, was obviously getting worse. Knee deep in the water, I broke open the panels with a fire axe and pulled out the bales of weed that were under the water. I tossed them forward to Calvin who moved them up to safety.

I ran back up to the cabin and burst in. "You sank another one of my boats, you son-of-a-bitch!"

Even through his sunglasses, I could see that Halsten was panicked.

"It's not my fault this time," he said, holding his hands up in defense. "It's my name. It means "rock." It's a curse for a sailor to have such a name!"

"Can we make it to the dock?" I said quickly.

"I think so. I think-"

I cut him off, "Get us there."

Just then, I noticed he was holding the radio mic.

"Did you just radio somebody?" I said.

He paused. "The Coast Guard."

I exploded. "Are you serious? You called the Coast Guard?"

"Yes," he said, "I told them we are smugglers and we are sinking."

"What?" I yelled, "Why?"

But I didn't really want an answer. "Get us to Miami," I said, "And stay off the radio!"

I stormed back out of the cabin and ran to check the pumps. The water was a few inches deeper. The pumps were helping, but the flow was getting ahead of them. It was a losing battle. I went back to work, grabbing bales of weed and tossing them up to Calvin. By the time I had all the bales up from the below, the water was waist-high. While Calvin was pulling bales of weed from the walls of the berths, I went above the deck. We were drifting past the Keys in the dwindling, orange sun, frantic to save the weed and not to attract attention to ourselves.

Just past the Keys, the boat seemed to sink an inch for every one that it gained toward the shore. Beginning to list to the right, we banged into the dock in Miami right at sundown. Water had filled the berths and was starting to cover the afterdeck.

Dennis was standing on the dock between two cargo vans, one grey and one dark blue that were backed to the water.

"Let's go!" he said having assessed the dire situation and knowing better than to stand there dumbstruck, "Toss them up!"

Halsten and Calvin scrambled and slipped their way forward carrying heavy bales of marijuana. Their frenzied work was made heavier and more cumbersome by the soaked wrapping of the bales. Dennis worked with another man to put the waterlogged bricks in the waiting vans, but I didn't see who it was.

Bales of marijuana were beginning to float above the spot where the cabin had sunk beneath the surface. Treading water, I pushed the bales toward the part of the bow that was still showing.

"Let's go! Come on!" Dennis yelled and waved his arm. Calvin was pushing the last two bales onto the dock as Halsten climbed out of the water.

"Here!" he yelled, reaching down to grab one of the bales from Calvin.

In the water, the last few feet of the bow were slipping out of sight. Through the panic, I kept count of the bales coming out of the water and I knew there was one more stuck on the boat somewhere.

"Forget it," answered Calvin.

"We gotta go!" yelled Dennis.

I was determined not to leave the job unfinished. I dove below the surface and pushed myself down through the dark water to the cabin. The weed had to be there. I swam inside, reached around, and felt it. The boat slid further downward, and I bumped my shoulder on the ship's wheel. I struggled with the bale to free it from where it was wedged alongside the captain's seat. It came loose and I clutched it to my side with one arm and pulled myself against the suction created by the sinking ship with the other. My lungs were beginning to burn as I kicked to the surface.

Gasping loudly, I pushed my face into the air. I did a hobbled sidestroke to the dock lugging the heavy bale. My body sank into the water as I pushed it upward to the screaming men on the dock. As I was climbing out of the water, something floated past in my peripheral vision. I turned to look. It was a paperback book. I pushed off against the dock and lunged for it. I threw it on the dock and climbed up after it.

"Come on! Get in!"

Drenched, Halsten and Calvin were sitting on opposite sides of the grey van full of wet bales of weed.

A pudgy face with a short, greasy beard looked back from the driver's window.

"Hurry!"

It was Fast Freddy. I jumped in the back of the van and as I shut the double doors, I saw the empty dock. It was as if no boat had ever been there.

I slammed the doors and the van jerked forward, accelerating quickly. Halsten, Calvin, and I swayed from side to side in the back as we sped away from the docks. I was breathing hard, dazed by the receding waves of panic and adrenaline.

"Dennis has the rest of the load in the other van," said Halsten bracing himself on the turns.

I nodded. I didn't know where we were going or why it was Fast Freddy who was taking us there. For a moment, no one said anything.

"I wonder why the Coast Guard didn't show up?" I said as much to myself as anyone.

"I didn't call them," said Halsten.

"What?" I said, "Why did you tell me you did?"

"To motivate you." He barely saved it from sounding like a

question.

I nodded and mulled that over when again, it caught my eye and I picked up Calvin' soaked copy of *Crime and Punishment*.

"Here you go," I said and tossed it to him.

He looked at the cover of the book, squeezed some water out of it, and then looked up at me.

"What about the boat?" he asked.

"I guess we'll just forget about it, like last time," I said and cut my eyes at Halsten.

"The police will find this one," he said.

"That's okay," I said, "It's registered to J.R. Camper."

"Who's he?" asked Calvin.

"Nobody."

26 - I DID IT MY WAY

At a warehouse in Hialeah, we met Dennis and cut one of the bales open. We all smiled with relief to see that the weed inside was dry. We then proceeded to divide the load. Fast Freddy and his gang were expanding their service supplying local dealers with weed and, with the understanding that it was last of its kind, he bought almost half the load on the spot. He drove it away into the night in the grey van.

As he would ordinarily, Dennis took the rest of the weed up to Atlanta and cities beyond. He said he would call Jorge and tell him to have somebody pick us up and take us to our hotel.

However, it was Jorge himself who showed up. He laughed when he saw us in our sopping wet condition.

"The damn thing just sank." I tried explaining it to him as he drove, but he kept laughing. "Look, all you need to know is that the weed is all okay."

"What are you going to do about it?" he asked getting on the interstate.

"About what? The boat?"

"Yeah."

"Probably just leave it," I said. "It's registered under an alias."

When we parked in front of my usual downtown Miami hotel, Calvin and Halsten thanked Jorge and got out of the car. They passed through automatic doors in front and I turned to Jorge.

"Well," I said shaking his hand, "Thanks, brother. Always a hoot."

His smiled faded. "So that's it," he said, "You're out."

"I'm out."

He sighed. "You were good," he said.

"I was the best," I said and got out of the car and shut the door.

Jorge said, "Stay in touch anyway."

"I will. Give my regards to your mom."

"I will," he said and turned up the radio. The tinted, automatic window raised and he drove off. Booming music faded into the night as he pulled into the empty street.

We made a million dollars on the final load. I gave Halsten and Ronnie each 150,000 dollars. I was paying each man on the crew 40,000, but I gave Calvin an extra ten for his brave service as first mate. What remained was almost half a million dollars. I flew back to Jamaica with 160,000 to pay the crew and enough extra to fly Ronnie, Indie and me back to Miami, first class and for good.

Ronnie's money would be waiting for him when we got there. Halsten and Calvin decided to stay in Miami too and invest in a go-cart track.

I got it through the underworld grapevine that for a while the crew which stayed in Jamaica kept living on the farm and kept growing world class indica, but, with no means of transporting it, they had no way to control exportation and distribution. As a result, their profits took a deep hit. The best they could do was to sell their product to the journeyman smugglers and crooks that had no regard for quality and came and went from the docks like the fog. The weed that had once been considered the best outdoor weed in the world was now lumped together with all the other, unremarkable, commercial weed being grown in the region. And there was no way in the world a pirate was going to pay 600 dollars a pound for weed, no matter what color it was.

Where the crew had been making 36,000 dollars a year working for me, they ended up making only 12,000 and, eventually, the yields got smaller and the quality suffered. The salad days had come to a withering end, as salad days always do.

I wouldn't have minded running into Fast Freddy again, but I never did. He was killed one, misty dawn riding his motorcycle, drunk on I-75.

The morning we left Jamaica for the final time, I carried Indie through the airport terminal and put her down at our gate. According to the schedule, our flight to Miami would be right on time. Ronnie was stretched out in a seat with his head back, waiting. The announcement came that the flight would soon begin boarding. People began to meander toward the gate and form a line.

I took Indie's hand and looked down.

"It's almost time to get on the airplane," I said to her, "Are you

ready?"

She nodded.

As we got in line, she looked up at me with her mother's eyes and said, "Who are we going to be today, Daddy?"

Made in the USA
Monee, IL
13 June 2022

97876345R00095